FOR ENGINEE

Mathematical Formulae for Engineering and Science Students

S. BARNETT and T. M. CRONIN
School of Mathematical Sciences, University of Bradford

FOURTH EDITION

Addison Wesley Longman Limited
Edinburgh Gate, Harlow
Essex CM20 2JE, England
and Associated Companies throughout the world.

First published 1971 by Bradford University Press
Second edition 1975
Third edition 1979
Fourth edition 1986 by Longman Group Limited
Reprinted by Longman Scientific & Technical 1987 (twice), 1988, 1989, 1991, 1992, 1995
Reprinted by Addison Wesley Longman 1997, 1998

British Library Cataloguing in Publication Data

Barnett, S.
Mathematical formulae.-- 4th ed.
1. Mathematics — Handbooks, manuals, etc.
I. Title II. Cronin, T.M. III. Barnett, S.
Mathematical formulae for engineering and science studies

510'.212 QA40

ISBN 0-582-44758-5

Library of Congress Cataloging-in-Publication Data

Barnett, S.
Mathematical formulae for engineering and science students.

Reprint. Originally published: Bradford: Bradford University Press, 1971.
Includes index.
1. Mathematics -- Formulae. I. Cronin. T.M. (Timothy Matthew), 1927- II. Title.
QA41.B25 1986 510'.212 86-21441
ISBN 0-470-20655-1 (USA only)

Printed in Malaysia, GPS

CONTENTS

PREFACE

This booklet provides in a single volume a selection of frequently used formulae from several different branches of mathematics. The user we have principally in mind is the engineering or science student on degree or diploma courses.

With the contents of mathematics syllabuses steadily increasing, a general tendency is to offset the extra work involved by allowing the use of books of tables of various kinds. These are usually works of reference, often with a specific field of application, being designed for the professional user and therefore too detailed for students. We do not know of any existing book which is restricted to what we believe to be sufficient for student needs. We have here attempted to remedy this deficiency by providing a concise selection of useful formulae covering a wide spectrum of mathematical topics. Though the provision of formulae is sometimes objected to by diehards, it corresponds well with real life where reference material is readily available. This fact is well accepted nowadays and such things as 'open book' examinations are becoming increasingly common. Finally, by virtue of the booklet's compactness, we trust that the accessibility of its contents will enable the teacher to dispense with some of the more formalistic parts of mathematics courses.

The material is standard and well known, but we have tried to keep the presentation clear and straightforward. We begin with common finite and infinite series, and identities involving hyperbolic and circular functions. We have been especially careful over inverse circular functions since some existing books are rather misleading in this respect. Next we devote considerable space to lists of indefinite integrals (which can be used to give derivatives), definite integrals and reduction formulae for integration. In choosing the integrals we have aimed to meet most of the requirements of potential users of this booklet, although any selection must to a certain extent be a personal one. The theme of integration is continued by tables of Laplace transforms and theorems, and some simple analytical techniques for solving differential equations. We then give definitions and some properties of matrices and determinants, and close with sections on numerical methods and elementary statistics.

Although we have occasionally inserted a little explanatory matter, we must stress that this booklet is merely a list of formulae, definitions and theorems, not a textbook. It is essential to refer to an appropriate source for background material in any situation where there is a danger of a formula being applied blindly, without an understanding of the principles involved.

We should like to thank those of our colleagues at Bradford University who have made helpful suggestions during the preparation of this work, in particular Professor J.B.Helliwell, Dr. D.B.Hunter, Mr. G.Eccles and Mr. J.Orriss. We are also very grateful to Mrs. Margaret Balmforth who typed the manuscript; since this has been reproduced photographically her painstaking efforts can be appreciated by each individual reader.

S.BARNETT
T.M.CRONIN
April 1971.

PREFACE TO SECOND EDITION

We have generally received favourable comments on the first edition from both students and staff, and accordingly we have made only minor improvements and amendments to the previous contents. For example, we give further discussion of $\cot^{-1}$ in Section 3.6, and the details for determining particular integrals in Section 5.5.2 have been clarified. Our main alterations consist of additional material which we hope will make the booklet even more useful. We have added three sections to the end of Chapter 1, a section on Fourier series and related formulae to Chapter 4, and a section on Chebyshev polynomials to Chapter 9. There is also a new chapter on commonly used formulae for areas, volumes and moments of inertia. Finally, we have appended numerical tables of logarithmic, trigonometric and other functions. These latter are reproduced from *Four-Figure Mathematical Tables* by Frank Castle, by permission of Macmillan, London and Basingstoke, and St. Martin's Press Inc., New York.

We should like to thank Dr. J.A. Grant and Dr. R.E. Scraton for comments on Chapter 9, and of course Mrs. Margaret Balmforth who has continued her superlative efforts.

PREFACE TO THIRD EDITION

The need to produce a further edition has provided the opportunity to add an index, which will, it is hoped, make the booklet even more useful to students.

PREFACE TO FOURTH EDITION

Several generations of students have now utilised our book, which still remains the only one of its type to provide most of the commonly used mathematical formulae at university and college level in a compact and easy to use form. We have therefore left the major part of the text unaltered, but have provided new sections on z-tranforms (Chapter 6), matrix algebra (Chapter 8) and orthogonal polynomials and Walsh functions (Chapter 9). We have also added material on maxima and minima of differentiable functions (Chapter 3) and Fourier transforms (Chapter 4), and a new list of symbols and notations (Chapter 0), together with some revisions to the sections on numerical solution of differential equations (Chapter 9). With the widespread availability of pocket calculators, tables of logarithms and other functions have become unnecessary. We have therefore replaced them with some frequently used statistical tables. We are grateful to the following for permission to reproduce copyright material: Associated Book Publishers (UK) Ltd. for table 3 from *Statistics for Technology* by C. Chatfield (pub. Chapman & Hall 1978); Hodder & Stoughton Educational for tables 6 & 7 from *Lanchester Short Statistical Tables* by G.R. Braithwaite & C.O.D. Titmus (first pub. 1967); Ellis Horwood Ltd. & the Biometrika Trustees for tables 1 & 2 from *Applied & Computational Statistics — A First Course* by K.D.C. Stoodley (pub. Ellis Horwood Ltd., Chichester, England 1984).

We should like to thank our colleagues Dr. R.G. Cameron and Dr. M.A. Kelmanson for their comments and assistance; Longman for taking over publication; and Mrs. Valerie Hunter who typed the new and revised material in her usual expert fashion.

S.B., T.M.C.
January 1986

0. SYMBOLS AND NOTATION

0.1 Symbols

$\in$	is a member of	$\notin$	is not a member of
$\subset$	is a subset of	A' or A^c	complement of a set A
$\cup$	union	$\cap$	intersection
$\emptyset$	empty set	U	universal set
N	the set of natural numbers	Z	the set of integers including zero
Z_m	the set of integers modulo m	Q	the set of rational numbers
R	the set of real numbers	C	the set of complex numbers
$\equiv$	equivalence	$\approx$	approximately equal to
$\sim$	relates to; or, is asymptotic to	$\neq$ or $<>$	is not equal to
$\propto$	is proportional to	$\triangleq$	corresponds to
$\leqslant$	is less than or equal to	$\geqslant$	is greater than or equal to
$\ll$	is much less than	$\gg$	is much greater than
$[x]$	the greatest integer $\leqslant x$; or, the integer part of x	$\{x\}$	the fractional part of x
$\lfloor x \rfloor$	the greatest integer $\leqslant x$	$\lceil x \rceil$	the smallest integer $\geqslant x$
$\langle x \rangle$	the nearest integer to x	$\Rightarrow$	implication
$\Leftrightarrow$	equivalence (logical)	A' or $\neg A$	not A
$\wedge$	conjunction (AND), logical product	$\vee$	disjunction (OR), logical sum
$\forall$	for all	$\exists$	there exists
$[a,b]$	$a \leqslant x \leqslant b$ closed interval	(a,b)	$a < x < b$ open interval
$(a,b]$	$a < x \leqslant b$	$[a,b)$	$a \leqslant x < b$
$a \mid b$	a divides b	$a \nmid b$	a does not divide b
$\equiv$	congruence	$\langle x \rangle_m$	residue of x modulo m
(m,n)	greatest common divisor of m and n (GCD)	$[m,n]$	least common multiple of m and n (LCM)

0.1	Symbols (cont...)		
$\pi(x)$	number of primes $\leqslant x$	$\phi(n)$	Euler's totient function
!	factorial	!!	semi-factorial
$\sum$	sum	Π	product
$\lVert x \rVert$	norm of x	$\partial\Gamma$	boundary of region Γ
δ_{ij}	Kronecker delta	e_{ijk}	alternating tensor
$\delta(t)$	Dirac delta function	$H(t)$	step function
O, o	order of magnitude symbols	$\text{sign}(x)$	sign function
A^T	transpose of matrix	A^{-1}	inverse of matrix
A^*	conjugate transpose	$A \otimes B$	Kronecker product
$\underline{a}.\underline{b}$	scalar, or dot, product of vectors	$\underline{a} \times \underline{b}$ or $\underline{a} \wedge \underline{b}$	vector product
$[\underline{a}\ \underline{b}\ \underline{c}]$	scalar triple product	$\lvert\underline{a}\rvert$	modulus of vector $\underline{a}$
∇	differential vector operator	$\nabla\phi$	gradient of ϕ, grad ϕ
$\nabla.\underline{F}$	divergence of $\underline{F}$, div $\underline{F}$	$\nabla \times \underline{F}$	curl of $\underline{F}$, curl $\underline{F}$
∇^2	Laplacian operator	⩩	vector Laplacian
Δ	forward difference	∇	backward difference
δ	central difference	E	displacement
μ	average	D	differentiation

0.2	Greek alphabet		
A α alpha	H η eta	N ν nu	T τ tau
B β beta	Θ θ theta	Ξ ξ xi	Υ υ upsilon
Γ γ gamma	I ι iota	O o omicron	Φ ϕ phi
Δ δ delta	K κ kappa	Π π pi	X χ chi
E ε epsilon	Λ λ lambda	R ρ rho	Ψ ψ psi
Z ζ zeta	M μ mu	Σ σ sigma	Ω ω omega

0.3 Some additional definitions and notations

0.3.1 Solid angle

The solid angle of a conical region, vertex O, is measured by the area it cuts out on the surface of a unit sphere centered at O.

0.3.2 Congruence

$\langle x \rangle_m$ = residue (remainder) of x on division by m.

$$a \equiv b \bmod m \iff \langle a \rangle_m = \langle b \rangle_m$$

0.3.3 Factorials

$n! = n(n-1)(n-2) \ldots 3.2.1.$

$(2n)!! = 2n(2n-2)(2n-4) \ldots 4.2 = 2^n n!$

$(2n+1)!! = (2n+1)(2n-1) \ldots 5.3.1.$

0.3.4 Tensor symbols

δ_{ij} or $\delta_i^j = 1$, if $i = j$; $= 0$ if $i \neq j$.

$e_{ijk} = 1$, if ijk is a cyclic permutation of 1, 2, 3

$= -1$, if ijk is a cyclic permutation of 3, 2, 1

$= 0$, otherwise.

0.3.5 Special functions

Dirac delta function $\delta(t) = 0, \quad t \neq 0$

$$\int_{-\infty}^{\infty} \delta(t)dt = 1.$$

Step function $H(t) = 0, \quad t < 0$

$= 1, \quad t > 0.$

Sign function $\operatorname{sign}(x) = -1$, if $x < 0$

$= +1$, if $x > 0$.

0.3.6 Order of magnitude symbols

$f(x) = O[g(x)] \Rightarrow |f(x)| < C|g(x)|$, C positive constant.

$f(x) = o[g(x)] \Rightarrow \lim_{x\to\infty} [f(x)/g(x)] = 0.$

1. SERIES AND RELATED FORMULAE

1.1 Taylor's Theorem for a function of a single variable

$$f(a+h) = f(a) + hf'(a) + \frac{h^2 f''(a)}{2!} + \ldots + \frac{h^{n-1} f^{(n-1)}(a)}{(n-1)!} + R_n$$

where for a suitable value of θ between 0 and 1, the remainder after n terms is

$$R_n = \frac{h^n f^{(n)}(a+\theta h)}{n!}, \text{ (Lagrange), or } \frac{(1-\theta)^{n-1}}{(n-1)!} h^n f^{(n)}(a+\theta h), \text{(Cauchy)}.$$

The case where $a = 0$ is often called *Maclaurin's Series.*

1.2 Taylor's Theorem for a function of several variables

$$f(x_1 + h_1, x_2 + h_2, \ldots) = f + Df + \frac{D^2 f}{2!} + \ldots + \frac{D^{n-1} f}{(n-1)!} + R_n$$

where $f = f(x_1, x_2, \ldots)$, $\quad D \equiv \left(h_1 \frac{\partial}{\partial x_1} + h_2 \frac{\partial}{\partial x_2} + \ldots \right)$

$$R_n = \frac{D^n f(x_1 + \theta_1 h_1, x_2 + \theta_2 h_2, \ldots)}{n!}, \quad 0 < \theta_i < 1, \quad i = 1,2,\ldots$$

1.3 Summable series

1.3.1 Binomial series

$$(1+x)^n = 1 + nx + \frac{n(n-1)}{2!} x^2 + \ldots + \frac{n(n-1)\ldots(n-r+1)}{r!} x^r + \ldots$$

The coefficient of x^r is denoted by $\binom{n}{r}$, ${}^nC_r$ or ${}_nC_r$, $(0! = 1)$.

The series terminates when n is a positive integer, otherwise it converges for $|x| < 1$, $n < 0$ and for $|x| \leqslant 1$ for $n > 0$.

If and only if n is a positive integer, $\binom{n}{r} = \frac{n!}{r!(n-r)!} = \binom{n}{n-r}$.

$$(a+b)^n = a^n\left(1 + \frac{b}{a}\right)^n = b^n\left(1 + \frac{a}{b}\right)^n$$

1.3.2 Sum of Arithmetic Progression (A.P.) to n terms

$$a + (a+d) + (a+2d) + \ldots + \left[a+(n-1)d\right] = \frac{n}{2}\left[2a+(n-1)d\right]$$

$$= \frac{n}{2}\left[\text{1st term} + \text{last term}\right]$$

1.3.3 Sum of Geometric Progression (G.P.) to n terms

$$S_n = a + ar + ar^2 + \dots + ar^{n-1} = \frac{a(1-r^n)}{1-r} = \frac{a(r^n-1)}{r-1}$$

Sum to infinity of a G.P.

If $|r| < 1$, $\qquad \lim_{n\to\infty} S_n = a/(1-r)$

1.3.4 Sums of powers of the natural numbers

$$\sum_{r=1}^{n} r = 1 + 2 + 3 + \dots + n = n(n+1)/2$$

$$\sum_{r=1}^{n} r^2 = 1^2 + 2^2 + 3^2 + \dots + n^2 = n(n+1)(2n+1)/6$$

$$\sum_{r=1}^{n} r^3 = 1^3 + 2^3 + 3^3 + \dots + n^3 = [n(n+1)/2]^2 = \left(\sum r\right)^2$$

$$\sum_{r=1}^{n} r^4 = 1^4 + 2^4 + 3^4 + \dots + n^4 = n(n+1)(2n+1)(3n^2+3n-1)/30$$

NOTE: The above results may be used to find the sum of a series whose n-th term is made up of integral powers of n.

e.g. $\qquad 4 + 9 + 18 + \dots + (2n^2 - n + 3)$

$$= \sum_{r=1}^{n} (2r^2 - r + 3) = 2\sum_{r=1}^{n} r^2 - \sum_{r=1}^{n} r + 3n$$

1.4 Common power series

1.4.1 $\quad e^x = 1 + x + \dfrac{x^2}{2!} + \dfrac{x^3}{3!} + \dots \qquad |x| < \infty$

1.4.2 $\quad \ln(1+x) = x - \dfrac{x^2}{2} + \dfrac{x^3}{3} - \dfrac{x^4}{4} + \dots \qquad -1 < x \leqslant 1$

1.4.3 $\quad \sin x = x - \dfrac{x^3}{3!} + \dfrac{x^5}{5!} - \dfrac{x^7}{7!} + \dots \qquad |x| < \infty$

1.4.4 $\quad \cos x = 1 - \dfrac{x^2}{2!} + \dfrac{x^4}{4!} - \dfrac{x^6}{6!} + \dots \qquad |x| < \infty$

1.4.5 $\quad \tan x = x + \dfrac{x^3}{3} + \dfrac{2x^5}{15} + \dfrac{17x^7}{315} + \dfrac{62x^9}{2835} + \dots \qquad |x| < \pi/2$

1.4.6 $\quad \operatorname{cosec} x = \dfrac{1}{x} + \dfrac{x}{6} + \dfrac{7x^3}{360} + \dfrac{31x^5}{15120} + \dfrac{127x^7}{604800} + \dots \qquad |x| < \pi$

1.4.7 $\quad \sec x = 1 + \dfrac{x^2}{2} + \dfrac{5x^4}{24} + \dfrac{61x^6}{720} + \dfrac{277x^8}{8064} + \dots \qquad |x| < \pi/2$

1.4.8 $\quad \cot x = \dfrac{1}{x} - \dfrac{x}{3} - \dfrac{x^3}{45} - \dfrac{2x^5}{945} - \dfrac{x^7}{4725} - \dots \qquad |x| < \pi$

1.4.9 $\sin^{-1} x = x + \frac{1}{2} \cdot \frac{x^3}{3} + \frac{1.3}{2.4} \cdot \frac{x^5}{5} + \frac{1.3.5}{2.4.6} \cdot \frac{x^7}{7} + \ldots$

$-\pi/2 \leqslant \sin^{-1} x \leqslant \pi/2, \ |x| < 1$

1.4.10 $\tan^{-1} x = x - \frac{x^3}{3} + \frac{x^5}{5} - \frac{x^7}{7} + \ldots \quad -\pi/4 < \tan^{-1} x < \pi/4, \ |x| < 1$

1.4.11 $\tan^{-1} x = \frac{\pi}{2} - x^{-1} + \frac{x^{-3}}{3} - \frac{x^{-5}}{5} + \frac{x^{-7}}{7} - \ldots \quad \pi/4 < x < \pi/2, \ x > 1$

1.4.11 and the series for all the other inverse circular functions can be obtained from 1.4.9 and 1.4.10 using relations in 2.7.

1.4.12 $\sinh x = x + \frac{x^3}{3!} + \frac{x^5}{5!} + \frac{x^7}{7!} + \ldots \quad |x| < \infty$

1.4.13 $\cosh x = 1 + \frac{x^2}{2!} + \frac{x^4}{4!} + \frac{x^6}{6!} + \ldots \quad |x| < \infty$

1.4.14 $\tanh x = x - \frac{x^3}{3} + \frac{2x^5}{15} - \frac{17x^7}{315} + \frac{62x^9}{2835} - \ldots \quad |x| < \pi/2$

1.4.15 $\operatorname{cosech} x = \frac{1}{x} - \frac{x}{6} + \frac{7x^3}{360} - \frac{31x^5}{15120} + \ldots \quad |x| < \pi$

1.4.16 $\operatorname{sech} x = 1 - \frac{x^2}{2!} + \frac{5x^4}{4!} - \frac{61x^6}{6!} + \frac{1385x^8}{8!} - \ldots \quad |x| < \pi/2$

1.4.17 $\coth x = \frac{1}{x} + \frac{x}{3} - \frac{x^3}{45} + \frac{2x^5}{945} - \frac{x^7}{4725} + \ldots \quad |x| < \pi$

1.4.18 $\sinh^{-1} x = x - \frac{1}{2} \cdot \frac{x^3}{3} + \frac{1.3}{2.4} \cdot \frac{x^5}{5} - \frac{1.3.5}{2.4.6} \cdot \frac{x^7}{7} + \ldots \quad |x| < 1$

1.4.19 $\sinh^{-1} x = \ln(2x) + \frac{1}{2} \cdot \frac{x^{-2}}{2} - \frac{1.3}{2.4} \cdot \frac{x^{-4}}{4} + \frac{1.3.5}{2.4.6} \cdot \frac{x^{-6}}{6} - \ldots \quad x > 1$

1.4.20 $\sinh^{-1} x = -\ln|2x| - \frac{1}{2} \cdot \frac{x^{-2}}{2} + \frac{1.3}{2.4} \cdot \frac{x^{-4}}{4} - \frac{1.3.5}{2.4.6} \cdot \frac{x^{-6}}{6} + \ldots$

$x < -1$

1.4.21 $\operatorname{cosech}^{-1} x = \sinh^{-1}(x^{-1})$

For $|x| > 1$, use 1.4.18; for $0 < x < 1$, use 1.4.19; for $-1 < x < 0$, use 1.4.20.

1.4.22 $\cosh^{-1} x = \pm\left[\ln(2x) - \frac{1}{2} \cdot \frac{x^{-2}}{2} - \frac{1.3}{2.4} \cdot \frac{x^{-4}}{4} - \frac{1.3.5}{2.4.6} \cdot \frac{x^{-6}}{6} - \ldots\right] \quad x > 1$

1.4.23 $\operatorname{sech}^{-1} x = \cosh^{-1}(x^{-1}) \quad 0 < x < 1$

1.4.24 $\tanh^{-1} x = x + \frac{x^3}{3} + \frac{x^5}{5} + \frac{x^7}{7} + \ldots \quad |x| < 1$

1.4.25 $\coth^{-1} x = \tanh^{-1}(x^{-1}) \quad |x| > 1$

1.5 Convergence tests

1.5.1 D'Alembert's Ratio Test for convergence of an infinite series $\sum_{n=1}^{\infty} u_n(x)$

If $$\lim_{n\to\infty} \left|\frac{u_{n+1}(x)}{u_n(x)}\right| = \ell(x)$$

then the series $\sum_{n=1}^{\infty} u_n(x)$ will be absolutely convergent for those values of x for which $\ell(x) < 1$, and divergent for those values of x which make $\ell(x) > 1$. For the values of x which make $\ell(x) = 1$ the test gives no result.

1.5.2 Leibnitz's Test for the convergence of an alternating series

If $a_n \geqslant a_{n+1} > 0$ and $\lim_{n\to\infty} a_n = 0$

the infinite series

$$a_1 - a_2 + a_3 - a_4 + \ldots \quad \text{is convergent .}$$

1.6 Remainder theorem

When a polynomial $P(x)$ is divided by $x - a$ the remainder is $P(a)$. Therefore $P(x)$ has a factor $x - a$ if and only if $P(a) = 0$.

1.7 Stirling's formula

For large n, $$n! \sim \sqrt{(2\pi)}\, n^{n+\frac{1}{2}} e^{-n} \left(1 + \frac{1}{12n} + \frac{1}{288n^2} + \ldots\right)$$

$$\ln n! \sim (n + \tfrac{1}{2})\ln n - n + \tfrac{1}{2}\ln(2\pi)$$

1.8 Algebra of sets

1.8.1 $A \cup A = A$

1.8.2 $A \cap A = A$

1.8.3 $A \cup B = B \cup A$

1.8.4 $A \cap B = B \cap A$

1.8.5 $A \cup (B \cup C) = (A \cup B) \cup C$

1.8.6 $A \cap (B \cap C) = (A \cap B) \cap C$

1.8.7 $A \cup (B \cap C) = (A \cup B) \cap (A \cup C)$

1.8.8 $A \cap (B \cup C) = (A \cap B) \cup (A \cap C)$

1.8.9 The *universal* set U $\quad A \cup U = U$, $\quad A \cap U = A$

1.8.10 The *empty* or *null* set $\emptyset$ $\quad A \cup \emptyset = A$, $\quad A \cap \emptyset = \emptyset$

1.8.11 The *complement* A' of a set A

$$A \cup A' = U\ , \qquad A \cap A' = \emptyset\ , \qquad (A')' = A\ ,$$
$$(A \cup B)' = A' \cap B', \qquad (A \cap B)' = A' \cup B', \qquad U' = \emptyset\ .$$

2. ELEMENTARY TRANSCENDENTAL FUNCTIONS

Logarithmic, exponential, circular and hyperbolic functions

Note: the power series expansions of these functions are to be found in Section 1.

2.1 Complex numbers. Definitions

2.1.1 $z = x + iy$ Cartesian form

2.1.2 $z = r(\cos\theta + i\sin\theta)$ Polar form

2.1.3 Complex conjugate of z: $\bar{z} = x - iy$

2.1.4 Modulus of z: $|z| = +(x^2+y^2)^{1/2} = r = (z\bar{z})^{1/2}$

2.1.5 Argument of z: Arg z or Amp $z = \theta$

2.1.6 Real part of z: $\mathcal{R}e(z) = x = r\cos\theta = (z+\bar{z})/2$

2.1.7 Imaginary Part of z: $Im(z) = y = r\sin\theta = (z-\bar{z})/2i$

2.2 Logarithmic formulae

2.2.1 $\ln x = \log_e x = \int_1^x \frac{dt}{t}$, $x > 0$, $e = 2.71828\ldots$

2.2.2 $\log_a x = \ln x/\ln a$

2.2.3 $\log_b x = \log_a x/\log_a b$

2.2.4 $\ln x_1 x_2 = \ln x_1 + \ln x_2$

2.2.5 $\ln(x_1/x_2) = \ln x_1 - \ln x_2$

2.2.6 $\ln x^n = n\ln x$

2.2.7 $\ln e = 1$

2.3 Exponential formulae

2.3.1 If $\ln y = x$ then $y = \exp x$ or $y = e^x$

2.3.2 $\ln[\exp(x)] = x$

2.3.3 $\exp(\ln x) = x$

2.3.4 $a^x = \exp(x\ln a)$

2.4 Relationship between exponential and circular functions

2.4.1 $\cos z = (e^{iz} + e^{-iz})/2$

2.4.2 $\sin z = (e^{iz} - e^{-iz})/2i$

2.4.3 $e^{iz} = \cos z + i\sin z$

2.4.4 $e^{-iz} = \cos z - i\sin z$

2.4.5 $z = x + iy = r\cos\theta + ir\sin\theta = r(\cos\theta + i\sin\theta) = re^{i\theta}$

2.4.6 $$\tan z = \frac{e^{iz} - e^{-iz}}{i(e^{iz} + e^{-iz})} = \frac{1}{i}\cdot\frac{e^{2iz}-1}{e^{2iz}+1} = \frac{1}{i}\cdot\frac{1-e^{-2iz}}{1+e^{-2iz}}$$

2.4.7 De Moivre's Theorem

$(\cos z + i\sin z)^p = \cos pz + i\sin pz$ $(-\pi < \mathcal{R}e\, z \leqslant \pi$, unless p is an integer)

2.5 Circular Functions

2.5.1 $\tan z = \sin z/\cos z$

2.5.2 $\sec z = 1/\cos z$

2.5.3 $\cot z = 1/\tan z = \cos z/\sin z$

2.5.4 $\operatorname{cosec} z = 1/\sin z$

2.5.5 $\sin^2 z + \cos^2 z = 1$

2.5.6 $\sec^2 z - \tan^2 z = 1$

2.5.7 $\operatorname{cosec}^2 z - \cot^2 z = 1$

2.5.8 $\sin(-z) = -\sin z$

2.5.9 $\cos(-z) = \cos z$

2.5.10 $\tan(-z) = -\tan z$

Compound Formulae: sines and cosines

2.5.11 $\sin(a \pm b) = \sin a \cos b \pm \cos a \sin b$

2.5.12 $\cos(a \pm b) = \cos a \cos b \mp \sin a \sin b$ (note reversed signs)

2.5.13 $2 \sin a \cos b = \sin(a + b) + \sin(a - b)$

2.5.14 $2 \cos a \cos b = \cos(a - b) + \cos(a + b)$

2.5.15 $2 \sin a \sin b = \cos(a - b) - \cos(a + b)$

2.5.16 $\sin a + \sin b = 2 \sin \tfrac{1}{2}(a + b) \cos \tfrac{1}{2}(a - b)$

2.5.17 $\sin a - \sin b = 2 \cos \tfrac{1}{2}(a + b) \sin \tfrac{1}{2}(a - b)$

2.5.18 $\cos a + \cos b = 2 \cos \tfrac{1}{2}(a + b) \cos \tfrac{1}{2}(a - b)$

2.5.19 $\cos a - \cos b = 2 \sin \tfrac{1}{2}(a + b) \sin \tfrac{1}{2}(b - a)$ (Note reverse order in last term)

2.5.20 $\sin^2 a - \sin^2 b = \cos^2 b - \cos^2 a = \sin(a + b) \sin (a - b)$

2.5.21 $\cos^2 a - \sin^2 b = \cos^2 b - \sin^2 a = \cos(a + b) \cos (a - b)$

Multiple Angle Formulae: sines and cosines

2.5.22 $\sin 2z = 2 \sin z \cos z$

2.5.23 $\cos 2z = \cos^2 z - \sin^2 z = 2 \cos^2 z - 1 = 1 - 2 \sin^2 z$

2.5.24 $\sin 3z = 3 \sin z - 4 \sin^3 z$

2.5.25 $\cos 3z = 4 \cos^3 z - 3 \cos z$

2.5.26 $\sin nz = \sum_{r=0}^{n} \binom{n}{r} \sin \frac{r\pi}{2} \cos^{n-r} z \sin^r z$

2.5.27 $\cos nz = \sum_{r=0}^{n} \binom{n}{r} \cos \frac{r\pi}{2} \cos^{n-r} z \sin^r z$

} for positive integral n

Powers of sines and cosines

2.5.28 $\sin^2 z = \tfrac{1}{2} (1 - \cos 2z)$

2.5.29 $\cos^2 z = \tfrac{1}{2} (1 + \cos 2z)$

2.5.30 $\sin^3 z = \tfrac{1}{4} (3 \sin z - \sin 3z)$

2.5.31 $\cos^3 z = \tfrac{1}{4} (3 \cos z + \cos 3z)$

2.5.32 $\sin^n z = \frac{1}{2^n} \sum_{r=0}^{n} \binom{n}{r} \cos(n - 2r)\left(\frac{\pi}{2} - z\right)$

2.5.33 $\cos^n z = \frac{1}{2^n} \sum_{r=0}^{n} \binom{n}{r} \cos(n - 2r)z$

} for positive integral n

Compound Formula for tan

2.5.34 $$\tan(a \pm b) = \frac{\tan a \pm \tan b}{1 \mp \tan a \tan b}$$

2.5.35 Signs of the principal circular functions in the four quadrants

Sine only positive	**A**ll positive
Tan only positive	**C**os only positive

Note mnemonic CAST

The functions cosec, sec and cot take the signs of their respective reciprocals.

2.5.36 Values of the circular functions for some special angles

$$\sin n\pi = 0 \qquad \cos n\pi = (-1)^n \qquad \text{for integers } n$$

The circular functions of $\pi/4 = 45^\circ$, $\pi/3 = 60^\circ$, $\pi/6 = 30^\circ$ can be read off from the right-angled triangles below

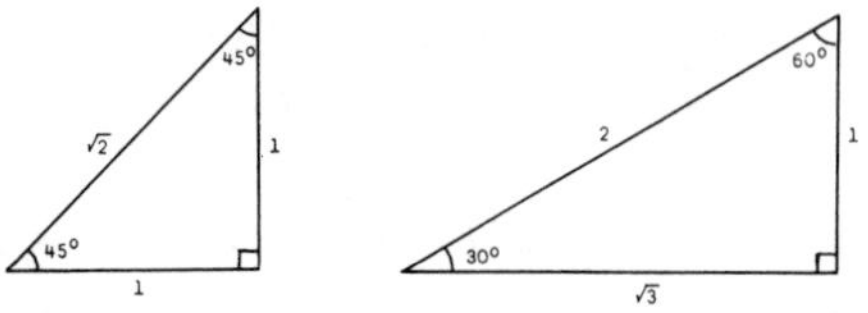

2.6 Formulae for plane triangles, with angles A,B,C and opposite sides a,b,c respectively

2.6.1 Sine Rule

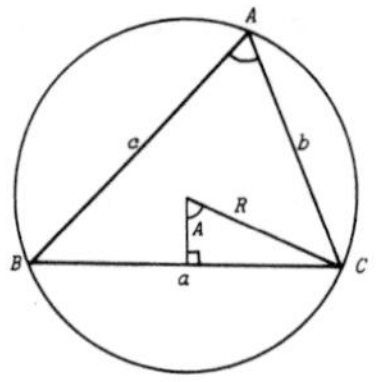

$$\frac{a}{\sin A} = \frac{b}{\sin B} = \frac{c}{\sin C} = 2R$$

R = radius of circumcircle.

2.6.2 Cosine Rule $a^2 = b^2 + c^2 - 2bc \cos A$.

2.6.3 Area of triangle $= \frac{1}{2}bc \sin A$

$$= \sqrt{s(s-a)(s-b)(s-c)} \text{ where } 2s = a + b + c.$$

2.7 Inverse circular functions, real variable only

In order to define a unique inverse function, it is necessary to restrict it to a range of values for which the original function is strictly monotonic, for example a suitable range for $\sin^{-1}$ is $[-\pi/2, \pi/2]$, for $\cos^{-1}$ $[0, \pi]$, while either would suit $\tan^{-1}$. Although there are no generally accepted definitions for all these functions those given here are probably more widely used than any other. Ranges which give unique derivatives for $\sec^{-1}$ and cosec^{-1} are sometimes chosen but these introduce additional complications.

Principal values and properties of $\sin^{-1}$ and $\operatorname{cosec}^{-1}$

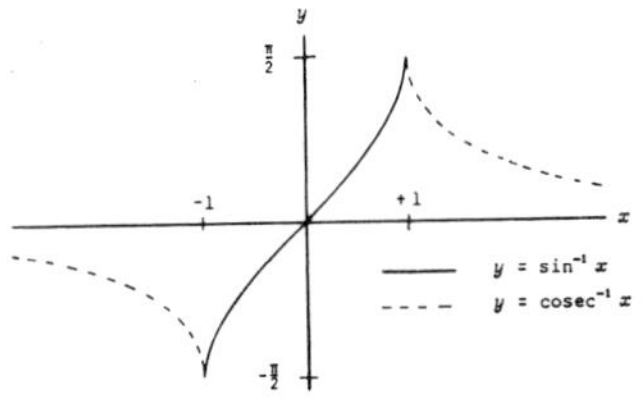

2.7.1	$-\pi/2 \leqslant \sin^{-1} x \leqslant \pi/2$	$\lvert x\rvert \leqslant 1$
2.7.2	$-\pi/2 \leqslant \operatorname{cosec}^{-1} x < 0$ and $0 < \operatorname{cosec}^{-1} x \leqslant \pi/2$	$\lvert x\rvert \geqslant 1$
2.7.3	$\operatorname{cosec}^{-1} x = \sin^{-1} 1/x$	$x \neq 0$
2.7.4	$\sin^{-1}(-x) = -\sin^{-1} x$	
2.7.5	$\operatorname{cosec}^{-1}(-x) = -\operatorname{cosec}^{-1} x$	

Principal values and properties of $\cos^{-1}$ and $\sec^{-1}$

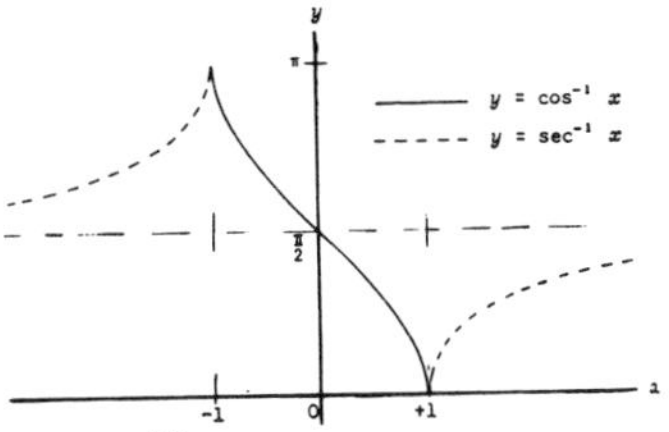

2.7.6	$0 \leqslant \cos^{-1} x \leqslant \pi$	$\lvert x\rvert \leqslant 1$
2.7.7	$0 \leqslant \sec^{-1} x < \pi/2$ and $\pi/2 < \sec^{-1} x \leqslant \pi$	$\lvert x\rvert \geqslant 1$
2.7.8	$\sec^{-1} x = \cos^{-1} 1/x$	$x \neq 0$
2.7.9	$\cos^{-1}(-x) = \pi - \cos^{-1} x$	
2.7.10	$\sec^{-1}(-x) = \pi - \sec^{-1} x$	

Principal values and properties of $\tan^{-1}$ and $\cot^{-1}$

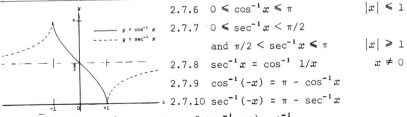

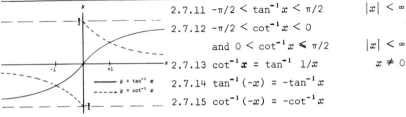

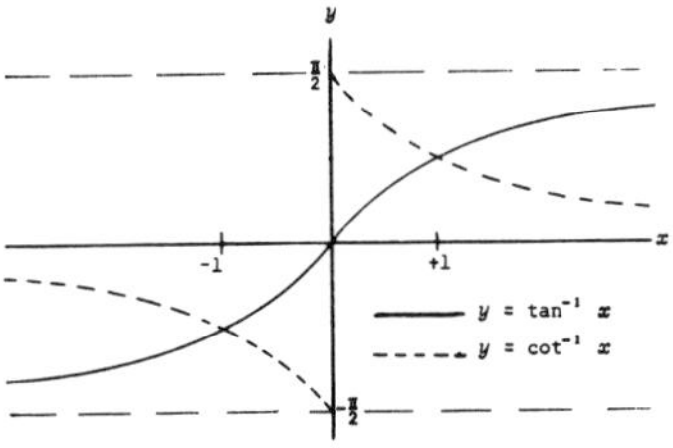

2.7.11	$-\pi/2 < \tan^{-1} x < \pi/2$	$\lvert x\rvert < \infty$
2.7.12	$-\pi/2 < \cot^{-1} x < 0$ and $0 < \cot^{-1} x \leqslant \pi/2$	$\lvert x\rvert < \infty$
2.7.13	$\cot^{-1} x = \tan^{-1} 1/x$	$x \neq 0$
2.7.14	$\tan^{-1}(-x) = -\tan^{-1} x$	
2.7.15	$\cot^{-1}(-x) = -\cot^{-1} x$	

Relations between functions

2.7.16 $\sin^{-1} x + \cos^{-1} x = \pi/2$

2.7.17 $\operatorname{cosec}^{-1} x + \sec^{-1} x = \pi/2$

2.7.18 $\tan^{-1} x + \cot^{-1} x = \pi/2 \quad x \geqslant 0$
$\qquad = -\pi/2 \quad x < 0$

2.7.19 $\tan^{-1} x \pm \tan^{-1} y = \tan^{-1} \dfrac{x \pm y}{1 \mp xy}$

Principal values as defined above are used in 2.7.1 - 18 and the relations given do not necessarily hold if other principal values are taken. For an alternative principal value for $\cot^{-1} x$ which is not discontinuous at $x = 0$, see 3.6.

2.8 Hyperbolic Functions: definitions and relation to circular functions

2.8.1	$\cosh z = \dfrac{e^z + e^{-z}}{2}$	2.8.2	$\sinh z = \dfrac{e^z - e^{-z}}{2}$
2.8.3	$\operatorname{sech} z = 1/\cosh z$	2.8.4	$\operatorname{cosech} z = 1/\sinh z$
2.8.5	$\tanh z = \sinh z/\cosh z$	2.8.6	$\coth z = 1/\tanh z$
2.8.7	$\sin iz = i \sinh z$	2.8.8	$\cos iz = \cosh z$
2.8.9	$\sinh iz = i \sin z$	2.8.10	$\cosh iz = \cos z$

Similar relations between the other circular and hyperbolic functions can be obtained from 2.8.7 - 2.8.10 using the appropriate definitions.

2.9 Hyperbolic Functions: Formulae.

Results involving hyperbolic functions can be deduced from the corresponding trigonometric relations 2.5 by replacing z by iz and using 2.8.7. - 2.8.10 and results derived from them. This method is sometimes stated in a form known as *Osborne's rule*: To derive an hyperbolic identity from the corresponding trigonometric one express the formula in terms of sin and cos and replace every cos by cosh, every sin by $i$sinh.

Examples

(1) $\sin(a + b) = \sin a \cos b + \cos a \sin b$

$\rightarrow i \sinh(a + b) = i \sinh a \cosh b + \cosh a \, i \sinh b.$

i.e. $\sinh(a + b) = \sinh a \cosh b + \cosh a \sinh b$

(2) $\sin^2 z + \cos^2 z = 1$

$\rightarrow (i \sinh z)^2 + (\cosh z)^2 = 1$ i.e. $\cosh^2 z - \sinh^2 z = 1.$

2.9.1 Compound Formula for tanh

$$\tanh(a \pm b) = \frac{\tanh a \pm \tanh b}{1 \pm \tanh a \tanh b}$$

2.10 Inverse Hyperbolic Functions

2.10.1. $$\sinh^{-1} x/a = \ln\left[(x + \sqrt{x^2+a^2})/a\right] = \tanh^{-1} \frac{x}{\sqrt{x^2+a^2}}$$
$$= \pm \cosh^{-1} \frac{\sqrt{x^2+a^2}}{a} \quad \begin{pmatrix} +, & x>0 \\ -, & x<0 \end{pmatrix}$$

2.10.2. $$\cosh^{-1} x/a = \pm \ln\left[(x + \sqrt{x^2-a^2})/a\right] = \pm \tanh^{-1} \frac{\sqrt{x^2-a^2}}{x}$$
$$= \pm \sinh^{-1} \frac{\sqrt{x^2-a^2}}{a}, \quad x \geqslant a$$

2.10.3. $$\tanh^{-1} x/a = \tfrac{1}{2} \ln\left(\frac{a+x}{a-x}\right), \quad |x| < a$$

2.10.4. $$\operatorname{cosech}^{-1} x/a = \ln\left[(a + \sqrt{a^2+x^2})/x\right]$$

2.10.5 $$\operatorname{sech}^{-1} x/a = \pm\ln\left[(a + \sqrt{a^2-x^2})/x\right], \quad 0 < x < a$$

2.10.6 $\operatorname{cosech}^{-1} x = \sinh^{-1} \frac{1}{x}$ 2.10.7 $\operatorname{sech}^{-1} x = \cosh^{-1} \frac{1}{x}$

2.10.8 $\coth^{-1} x = \tanh^{-1} \frac{1}{x}$ 2.10.9 $\sinh^{-1}(-x) = -\sinh^{-1}(x)$

2.10.10 $\cosh^{-1}(-x) = \cosh^{-1} x$ 2.10.11 $\tanh^{-1}(-x) = -\tanh^{-1} x$

3. INTEGRALS AND DERIVATIVES

The following tables, when read from left to right, give integrals of functions $f(x)$ (the constant of integration is omitted); when read from right to left they also give derivatives of functions $F(x)$.

	Function $f(x)$ $\longrightarrow$ Derivative $\frac{dF}{dx}$ $\longleftarrow$	Integral $\int f(x)dx$ Function $F(x)$
3.1.	**Rational algebraic functions**	
1	$x^n, \quad n \neq -1$	$x^{n+1}/(n+1)$
2	$1/x$	$\ln\lvert x\rvert$
3	$(a+bx)^n, \quad n \neq -1$	$(a+bx)^{n+1}/b(n+1)$
4	$1/(a+bx)$	$(1/b)\ln\lvert a+bx\rvert$
5	$x/(a+bx)$	$(a+bx-a\ln\lvert a+bx\rvert)/b^2$
6	$x/(a+bx)^2$	$\left[\ln\lvert a+bx\rvert + a/(a+bx)\right]/b^2$
7	$x/(a+bx)^n$ $n \neq 1,2$	$\frac{1}{b^2}\left[\frac{-1}{(n-2)(a+bx)^{n-2}} + \frac{a}{(n-1)(a+bx)^{n-1}}\right]$
8	$(e+fx)^m/(a+bx)^n$ m,n positive integers	Substitute $u = a+bx$ and expand the numerator using 1.3.1.
9	$1/x^m(a+bx)^n$, m,n positive integers	Substitute $u = (a+bx)/x$ and expand the resulting numerator using 1.3.1.
10	$1/(a^2+x^2), \quad a > 0$	$(1/a)\tan^{-1}(x/a)$ (principal value)
11	$1/(a^2+x^2)^2, \quad a > 0$	$x/\left[2a^2(a^2+x^2)\right] + (1/2a^3)\tan^{-1}(x/a)$
12	$1/(a^2-x^2), \quad a > 0$	$\frac{1}{2a}\ln\frac{a+x}{a-x} = \frac{1}{a}\tanh^{-1}\frac{x}{a}, \quad \lvert x\rvert < a$ $\frac{1}{2a}\ln\frac{x+a}{x-a} = \frac{1}{a}\coth^{-1}\frac{x}{a}, \quad \lvert x\rvert > a$
13	$1/(a^2-x^2)^2, \quad a > 0$	$\frac{x}{2a^2(a^2-x^2)} + \frac{1}{4a^3}\ln\left\lvert\frac{a+x}{a-x}\right\rvert$

Function $f(x)$ $\longrightarrow$ Integral $\int f(x)dx$ Derivative $\frac{dF}{dx}$ $\longleftarrow$ Function $F(x)$		
3.1.	**Rational algebraic functions (cont...)**	
14	$1/(ax^2+bx+c)$, where $d=b^2-4ac$	$\frac{2}{\sqrt{-d}}\tan^{-1}\frac{2ax+b}{\sqrt{-d}}$, $d<0$ $\frac{1}{\sqrt{d}}\ln\left\lvert\frac{2ax+b-\sqrt{d}}{2ax+b+\sqrt{d}}\right\rvert$, $d>0$ $-2/(2ax+b)$, $d=0$
15	$1/(ax^2+bx+c)^n$ $x^m/(ax^2+bx+c)^n$ $1/x(ax^2+bx+c)^n$ $(ax^2+bx+c)^n$	See 4.2.5 See 4.2.6 See 4.2.7 See 4.2.8
16	$1/(x^3+a^3)$, $a\neq 0$	$\frac{1}{6a^2}\ln\frac{(x+a)^2}{x^2-ax+a^2}+\frac{1}{a^2\sqrt{3}}\tan^{-1}\frac{2x-a}{a\sqrt{3}}$
17	$x/(x^3+a^3)$, $a\neq 0$	$\frac{1}{6a}\ln\frac{x^2-ax+a^2}{(x+a)^2}+\frac{1}{a\sqrt{3}}\tan^{-1}\frac{2x-a}{a\sqrt{3}}$
3.2.	**Irrational algebraic functions**	
1	$x/(a+bx)^k$, any $k\neq 1,2$ (see also 3.1.7)	$\frac{1}{b^2}\left[-\frac{1}{(k-2)(a+bx)^{k-2}}+\frac{a}{(k-1)(a+bx)^{k-1}}\right]$
2	$x^m/(a+bx)^k$, any k, m positive integer	Substitute $u=a+bx$ and expand the numerator using 1.3.1.
3	$1/x\sqrt{a+bx}$ [For $1/x(a+bx)^{n/2}$, see 4.2.4]	$\frac{1}{\sqrt{a}}\ln\left\lvert\frac{\sqrt{a+bx}-\sqrt{a}}{\sqrt{a+bx}+\sqrt{a}}\right\rvert$, $a>0$, $a+bx>0$ $-(2/\sqrt{a})\tanh^{-1}\sqrt{(a+bx)/a}$, $a>a+bx>0$ $-(2/\sqrt{a})\coth^{-1}\sqrt{(a+bx)/a}$, $a+bx>a>0$ $(2/\sqrt{-a})\tan^{-1}\sqrt{-(a+bx)/a}$, $a<0$, $a+bx>0$
4	$1/\sqrt{a^2-x^2}$	$\sin^{-1}(x/a)$ (principal value)

Function $f(x)$ $\longrightarrow$	Integral $\int f(x)dx$
Derivative $\frac{dF}{dx}$ $\longleftarrow$	Function $F(x)$

3.2. Irrational algebraic functions

5	$1/\sqrt{x^2 \pm a^2}$	$\ln\left\lvert x + \sqrt{x^2 \pm a^2}\right\rvert$ (see 2.10.1,2)
6	$\sqrt{a^2 - x^2}$	$\frac{1}{2}x\sqrt{a^2 - x^2} + \frac{1}{2}a^2 \sin^{-1}(x/a)$ (principal value)
7	$\sqrt{x^2 \pm a^2}$	$\frac{1}{2}x\sqrt{x^2 \pm a^2} \pm \frac{1}{2}a^2 \ln\left\lvert x + \sqrt{x^2 \pm a^2}\right\rvert$ (see 2.10.1,2)
8	$1/x\sqrt{a^2 \pm x^2}$	$-\frac{1}{a}\ln\left\lvert \frac{a + \sqrt{a^2 \pm x^2}}{x}\right\rvert$ (see 2.10.4,5)
9	$1/x\sqrt{x^2 - a^2}$	$\frac{1}{a}\sec^{-1}\left\lvert\frac{x}{a}\right\rvert = \frac{1}{a}\cos^{-1}\left\lvert\frac{a}{x}\right\rvert$, (principal values), $\lvert x\rvert > \lvert a\rvert$
10	$1/\sqrt{ax^2 + bx + c}$ where $d = b^2 - 4ac$	$\frac{1}{\sqrt{a}}\ln\left\lvert 2\sqrt{a(ax^2 + bx + c)} + 2ax + b\right\rvert$, $a > 0$, $d \neq 0$ $\frac{-1}{\sqrt{-a}}\sin^{-1}\frac{(2ax + b)}{\sqrt{d}}$ (principal value) $a < 0, d > 0$, $\lvert 2ax + b\rvert < \sqrt{d}$
11	$\sqrt{ax^2 + bx + c}$, where $d = b^2 - 4ac$	$\frac{(2ax + b)\sqrt{ax^2 + bx + c}}{4a} - \frac{d}{8a}\int\frac{dx}{\sqrt{ax^2 + bx + c}}$ (see 3.2.10)
12	$x\sqrt{ax^2 + bx + c}$, where $d = b^2 - 4ac$	$\frac{-b(2ax + b)\sqrt{ax^2 + bx + c}}{8a^2} + \frac{bd}{16a^2}\int\frac{dx}{\sqrt{ax^2 + bx + c}}$ $+ (1/3a)(ax^2 + bx + c)^{3/2}$ (see 3.2.10)
13	$1/x\sqrt{ax^2 + bx + c}$	Substitute $u = 1/x$ to obtain $-\int\frac{du}{\sqrt{cu^2 + bu + a}}$ (see 3.2.10)

Function $f(x)$ $\longrightarrow$ Integral $\int f(x)dx$

Derivative $\frac{dF}{dx}$ $\longleftarrow$ Function $F(x)$

3.3. Trigonometric functions

1	$\sin x$	$-\cos x$
2	$\cos x$	$\sin x$
3	$\tan x$	$-\ln\lvert\cos x\rvert = \ln\lvert\sec x\rvert$
4	$\operatorname{cosec} x$	$\ln\lvert\tan \frac{1}{2}x\rvert = \frac{1}{2}\ln\left(\frac{1-\cos x}{1+\cos x}\right)$ $= \ln\lvert\operatorname{cosec} x - \cot x\rvert$
5	$\sec x$	$\ln\lvert\tan(\pi/4 + x/2)\rvert = \frac{1}{2}\ln\left(\frac{1+\sin x}{1-\sin x}\right)$ $= \ln\lvert\sec x + \tan x\rvert$
6	$\cot x$	$\ln\lvert\sin x\rvert$
7	$\sec^2 x$	$\tan x$
8	$\operatorname{cosec} x \cot x$	$-\operatorname{cosec} x$
9	$\sec x \tan x$	$\sec x$
10	$\operatorname{cosec}^2 x$	$-\cot x$
11	$\operatorname{cosec} x \sec x$	$\ln\lvert\tan x\rvert$
12	$\tan^2 x$	$\tan x - x$
13	$1/(1+\sin x)$	$-\tan(\pi/4 - x/2)$
14	$1/(1-\sin x)$	$\tan(\pi/4 + x/2)$
15	$1/(1+\cos x)$	$\tan \frac{1}{2}x$
16	$1/(1-\cos x)$	$-\cot \frac{1}{2}x$

Function $f(x)$ $\longrightarrow$	Integral $\int f(x)dx$
Derivative $\frac{dF}{dx}$ $\longleftarrow$	Function $F(x)$

3.3. Trigonometric functions (cont...)

17	$\begin{smallmatrix}\sin\\\cos\end{smallmatrix} nx \begin{smallmatrix}\sin\\\cos\end{smallmatrix} mx$	use 2.5.13 - 15
18	$\sin^n x$, $\cos^n x$, $\tan^n x$, $\operatorname{cosec}^n x$, $\sec^n x$, $\cot^n x$. n positive integer	see 2.5.32,33 and 4.2.1.
19	$\sin^m x \cos^n x$	Put $u = \cos x$, m odd; $u = \sin x$, n odd } or both. Use 2.5.28.29 if m,n both even
20	$\sin^m x \cos^n x$, m,n integers	see 4.2.2.
21	Rational function of $\sin x$ and $\cos x$	Use the substitution $t = \tan(x/2)$, $\sin x = 2t/(1+t^2)$, $\cos x = (1-t^2)/(1+t^2)$, $dx/dt = 2/(1+t^2)$
22	$\sin^{-1}(x/a)$, $a > 0$	$x \sin^{-1}(x/a) + \sqrt{a^2 - x^2}$
23	$\cos^{-1}(x/a)$, $a > 0$	$x \cos^{-1}(x/a) - \sqrt{a^2 - x^2}$
24	$\tan^{-1}(x/a)$	$x \tan^{-1}(x/a) - (a/2)\ln(a^2 + x^2)$
25	$\operatorname{cosec}^{-1}(x/a)$	$x \operatorname{cosec}^{-1}(x/a) \pm a \ln\|x + \sqrt{x^2 - a^2}\|$, (+ if $0 < \operatorname{cosec}^{-1}(x/a) \leqslant \pi/2$) (- if $-\frac{\pi}{2} \leqslant \operatorname{cosec}^{-1}(x/a) < 0$)
26	$\sec^{-1}(x/a)$	$x \sec^{-1}(x/a) \mp a \ln\|x + \sqrt{x^2 - a^2}\|$ (- if $0 \leqslant \sec^{-1}(x/a) < \pi/2$) (+ if $\pi/2 < \sec^{-1}(x/a) \leqslant \pi$)
27	$\cot^{-1}(x/a)$	$x \cot^{-1}(x/a) + (a/2)\ln(a^2 + x^2)$

Function $f(x)$ $\longrightarrow$ Integral $\int f(x)dx$ Derivative $\frac{dF}{dx}$ $\longleftarrow$ Function $F(x)$		
3.4. Exponential and logarithmic functions		
1	e^{ax}	e^{ax}/a
2	$a^x, \quad a > 0$	$a^x/\ln a$
3	$x^n e^{ax}$, n non-negative integer For non-integral n, see 4.4.6. See also 4.7.7.	$e^{ax}\left[\frac{x^n}{a} - \frac{nx^{n-1}}{a^2} + \frac{n(n-1)x^{n-2}}{a^3} - \ldots + (-1)^{n-1}\frac{n!x}{a^n} + (-1)^n\frac{n!}{a^{n+1}}\right]$
4	$e^{ax}\sin bx$	$e^{ax}(a \sin bx - b \cos bx)/(a^2 + b^2)$
5	$e^{ax}\cos bx$	$e^{ax}(a \cos bx + b \sin bx)/(a^2 + b^2)$
6	$\ln ax, \quad ax > 0$	$x\ln(ax) - x$
7	$x^k \ln(ax)$ $k \neq -1, \quad ax > 0$	$\left[x^{k+1}/(k+1)\right]\ln(ax) - x^{k+1}/(k+1)^2$
8	$x^m(\ln x)^n$ For integers $m(\neq -1)$, $n > 0$	See 4.2.3.
9	$\ln\left(x + \sqrt{x^2 \pm a^2}\right)$, $x > 0$	$x\ln\left(x + \sqrt{x^2 \pm a^2}\right) - \sqrt{x^2 \pm a^2}$
3.5. Hyperbolic functions		
1	$\sinh x$	$\cosh x$
2	$\cosh x$	$\sinh x$
3	$\tanh x$	$\ln(\cosh x)$
4	$\operatorname{cosech} x$	$\ln\lvert\tanh \frac{1}{2}x\rvert = \frac{1}{2}\ln\left(\frac{\cosh x - 1}{\cosh x + 1}\right)$ $= -\ln\lvert\operatorname{cosech} x + \coth x\rvert = \ln\left(\frac{e^x - 1}{e^x + 1}\right)$

	Function $f(x)$ ⟶ Integral $\int f(x)dx$ Derivative $\frac{dF}{dx}$ ⟵ Function $F(x)$	
3.5.	Hyperbolic functions (cont...)	
5	sech x	$\tan^{-1}(\sinh x)$ or $2\tan^{-1}(e^x)$
6	coth x	$\ln\lvert\sinh x\rvert$
7	$\text{sech}^2 x$	tanh x
8	cosech x coth x	- cosech x
9	sech x tanh x	- sech x
10	$\text{cosech}^2 x$	- coth x
11	cosech x sech x	$\ln\lvert\tanh x\rvert$
12	$\tanh^2 x$	x - tanh x
13	1/(cosh x + 1)	tanh $\frac{1}{2}x$
14	1/(cosh x - 1)	- coth $\frac{1}{2}x$
15	$\frac{\sinh}{\cosh} nx \frac{\sinh}{\cosh} mx$	use 2.9
16	$\sinh^n x$, $\cosh^n x$, $\tanh^n x$, $\text{cosech}^n x$, $\text{sech}^n x$, $\coth^n x$. n positive integer	see 4.2.1.
17	$\sinh^m x \cosh^n x$, m,n positive integers	Put $u = \cosh x$, m odd $u = \sinh x$, n odd Use 2.9 and 2.5.28, 29 if m,n both even.
18	$\sinh^m x \cosh^n x$, m,n integers	see 4.2.2.

3.5.	Hyperbolic functions (cont...)	
19	$\sinh^{-1}(x/a),\ a > 0$	$x\sinh^{-1}(x/a) - \sqrt{a^2 + x^2}$
20	$\cosh^{-1}(x/a),\ a > 0$	$x\cosh^{-1}(x/a) - \sqrt{x^2 - a^2},\ \cosh^{-1}(x/a) > 0$ $x\cosh^{-1}(x/a) + \sqrt{x^2 - a^2},\ \cosh^{-1}(x/a) < 0$
21	$\tanh^{-1}(x/a)$	$x\tanh^{-1}(x/a) + (a/2)\ln(a^2 - x^2)$
22	$\operatorname{cosech}^{-1}(x/a)$	$x\operatorname{cosech}^{-1}(x/a) + a\sinh^{-1}(\|x\|/a)$
23	$\operatorname{sech}^{-1}(x/a)$	$x\operatorname{sech}^{-1}(x/a) + a\sin^{-1}(x/a),\ \operatorname{sech}^{-1}(x/a) > 0$ $x\operatorname{sech}^{-1}(x/a) - a\sin^{-1}(x/a),\ \operatorname{sech}^{-1}(x/a) < 0$
24	$\coth^{-1}(x/a)$	$x\coth^{-1}(x/a) + (a/2)\ln(x^2 - a^2)$

3.6 Maxima and minima of differentiable functions

3.6.1 Functions of one variable

$f(x)$ has a local extreme point at $x = x_0$ if $f^{2r-1}(x_0) = 0$ and $f^{2r}(x_0) \neq 0$, for $r \geqslant 1$, where $f^r(x_0) = \left[\frac{d^r f}{dx^r}\right]_{x = x_0}$

[in the simplest case $r = 1$ gives $f'(x_0) = 0$, $f''(x_0) \neq 0$].

The local extreme point is:

(i) a maximum if $f^{2r}(x_0) < 0$ (ii) a minimum if $f^{2r}(x_0) > 0$.

If $f^{2r}(x_0) = 0$ and $f^{2r+1}(x_0) \neq 0$, $r \geqslant 1$, x_0 is a point of *inflection*.

3.6.2 Functions of two variables

Writing $f_1(x_0,y_0)$, $f_2(x_0,y_0)$, $f_{11}(x_0,y_0)$, $f_{12}(x_0,y_0)$, $f_{22}(x_0,y_0)$ for $\frac{\partial f}{\partial x}$, $\frac{\partial f}{\partial y}$, $\frac{\partial^2 f}{\partial x^2}$, $\frac{\partial^2 f}{\partial x \partial y}$, $\frac{\partial^2 f}{\partial y^2}$ respectively, all evaluated at (x_0,y_0), then $f(x,y)$ has a *critical point* at (x_0,y_0) if $f_1(x_0,y_0) = f_2(x_0,y_0) = 0$. Defining

$$\Delta = \begin{vmatrix} f_{11}(x_0,y_0) & f_{12}(x_0,y_0) \\ f_{21}(x_0,y_0) & f_{22}(x_0,y_0) \end{vmatrix}$$

then the critical point (x_0,y_0) is:

(i) a local maximum if $\Delta > 0$ and $f_{11}(x_0,y_0)$ or $f_{22}(x_0,y_0) < 0$

(ii) a local minimum if $\Delta > 0$ and $f_{11}(x_0,y_0)$ or $f_{22}(x_0,y_0) > 0$

(iii) a local *saddle point* if $\Delta < 0$.

If $\Delta = 0$ a more detailed examination is necessary.

3.7 Derivatives of some inverse functions

	Function	Derivative
1	$\sin^{-1}(x/a)$	$1/\sqrt{a^2 - x^2}$ $\quad a > 0$
2	$\cos^{-1}(x/a)$	$-1/\sqrt{a^2 - x^2}$ $\quad a > 0$
3	$\tan^{-1}(x/a)$	$a/(a^2 + x^2)$ $\quad$ any a
4	$\operatorname{cosec}^{-1}(x/a)$	$-a/\|x\|\sqrt{x^2 - a^2}$ $\quad a > 0$
5	$\sec^{-1}(x/a)$	$a/\|x\|\sqrt{x^2 - a^2}$ $\quad a > 0$
6	$\cot^{-1}(x/a)$	$-a/(a^2 + x^2)$, $\quad x \neq 0$, $\quad$ any a
	The above results hold for principal values as defined in 2.7. However, in the case of $\cot^{-1}$ an alternative principal value is that defined by $0 < \cot^{-1}(x/a) < \pi$, and this has the advantages that for <u>all</u> x it is continuous and differentiable with continuous derivative $-a/(a^2 + x^2)$.	
7	$\sinh^{-1}(x/a)$	$1/\sqrt{a^2 + x^2}$
8	$\cosh^{-1}(x/a)$	$\pm 1/\sqrt{x^2 - a^2}$ $\quad \begin{cases} + \text{ if } \cosh^{-1}(x/a) > 0 \\ - \text{ if } \cosh^{-1}(x/a) < 0 \end{cases}$
9	$\tanh^{-1}(x/a)$	$a/(a^2 - x^2)$
10	$\operatorname{cosech}^{-1}(x/a)$	$-a/\|x\|\sqrt{x^2 + a^2}$
11	$\operatorname{sech}^{-1}(x/a)$	$\pm a/x\sqrt{a^2 - x^2}$ $\quad \begin{cases} - \text{ if } \operatorname{sech}^{-1}(x/a) > 0 \\ + \text{ if } \operatorname{sech}^{-1}(x/a) < 0 \end{cases}$
12	$\coth^{-1}(x/a)$	$a/(a^2 - x^2)$

See 2.10 for definitions of inverse hyperbolic functions.

4. INTEGRATION FORMULAE AND DEFINITE INTEGRALS

4.1 Integration by parts

For two functions $u(x)$, $v(x)$

$$\int_a^b u(x)v(x)dx = \Big[w(x)v(x)\Big]_a^b - \int_a^b w(x)v'(x)dx$$

where $w(x) = \int u(x)dx$, ignoring any constant of integration. A common alternative form is

$$\int_a^b u\, dv = [uv]_a^b - \int_a^b v\, du\ .$$

4.2 Reduction formulae

The following formulae are generally applied for integral values of m and n, so that the integration can be completed using the results in Section 3. In some cases, when $n < 0$, the reduction is obtained by reversing the formula (e.g. 4.2.3.)

4.2.1 For $n > 0$,

$$\int \sin^n x\, dx = -\frac{1}{n}\sin^{n-1}x\cos x + \frac{n-1}{n}\int \sin^{n-2}x\, dx$$

$$\int \cos^n x\, dx = \frac{1}{n}\cos^{n-1}x\sin x + \frac{n-1}{n}\int \cos^{n-2}x\, dx$$

$$\int \tan^n x\, dx = \frac{\tan^{n-1}x}{n-1} - \int \tan^{n-2}x\, dx \qquad (n \neq 1)$$

$$\int \operatorname{cosec}^n x\, dx = -\frac{\cos x\operatorname{cosec}^{n-1}x}{n-1} + \frac{n-2}{n-1}\int \operatorname{cosec}^{n-2}x\, dx \qquad (n \neq 1)$$

$$\int \sec^n x\, dx = \frac{\sin x\sec^{n-1}x}{n-1} + \frac{n-2}{n-1}\int \sec^{n-2}x\, dx \qquad (n \neq 1)$$

$$\int \cot^n x\, dx = -\frac{\cot^{n-1}x}{n-1} - \int \cot^{n-2}x\, dx \qquad (n \neq 1)$$

$$\int \sinh^n x\, dx = \frac{1}{n}\sinh^{n-1}x\cosh x - \frac{n-1}{n}\int \sinh^{n-2}x\, dx$$

$$\int \cosh^n x\, dx = \frac{1}{n}\cosh^{n-1}x\sinh x + \frac{n-1}{n}\int \cosh^{n-2}x\, dx$$

$$\int \tanh^n x\, dx = -\frac{\tanh^{n-1}x}{n-1} + \int \tanh^{n-2}x\, dx \qquad (n \neq 1)$$

$$\int \operatorname{cosech}^n x\, dx = -\frac{\cosh x\operatorname{cosech}^{n-1}x}{n-1} - \frac{n-2}{n-1}\int \operatorname{cosech}^{n-2}x\, dx \qquad (n \neq 1)$$

$$\int \operatorname{sech}^n x\,dx = \frac{\sinh x \operatorname{sech}^{n-1} x}{n-1} + \frac{n-2}{n-1}\int \operatorname{sech}^{n-2} x\,dx \qquad (n \neq 1)$$

$$\int \coth^n x\,dx = -\frac{\coth^{n-1} x}{n-1} + \int \coth^{n-2} x\,dx \qquad (n \neq 1)$$

4.2.2

$$\int \sin^m x \cos^n x\,dx = \frac{\sin^{m+1} x \cos^{n-1} x}{m+n} + \frac{n-1}{m+n}\int \sin^m x \cos^{n-2} x\,dx$$

$$= -\frac{\sin^{m-1} x \cos^{n+1} x}{m+n} + \frac{m-1}{m+n}\int \sin^{m-2} x \cos^n x\,dx$$

(m,n positive integers)

$$\int \frac{dx}{\sin^m x \cos^n x} = \frac{1}{(n-1)\sin^{m-1} x \cos^{n-1} x} + \frac{m+n-2}{n-1}\int \frac{dx}{\sin^m x \cos^{n-2} x}$$

($n > 1$, any m, positive or negative)

$$= \frac{-1}{(m-1)\sin^{m-1} x \cos^{n-1} x} + \frac{m+n-2}{m-1}\int \frac{dx}{\sin^{m-2} x \cos^n x}$$

($m > 1$, any n, positive or negative)

$$\int \sinh^m x \cosh^n x\,dx = \frac{\sinh^{m+1} x \cosh^{n-1} x}{m+n} + \frac{n-1}{m+n}\int \sinh^m x \cosh^{n-2} x\,dx$$

$$= \frac{\sinh^{m-1} x \cosh^{n+1} x}{m+n} - \frac{m-1}{m+n}\int \sinh^{m-2} x \cosh^n x\,dx$$

(m,n positive integers)

$$\int \frac{dx}{\sinh^m x \cosh^n x} = \frac{1}{(n-1)\sinh^{m-1} x \cosh^{n-1} x} + \frac{m+n-2}{n-1}\int \frac{dx}{\sinh^m x \cosh^{n-2} x}$$

($n > 1$, any m, positive or negative)

$$= \frac{-1}{(m-1)\sinh^{m-1} x \cosh^{n-1} x} - \frac{m+n-2}{m-1}\int \frac{dx}{\sinh^{m-2} x \cosh^n x}$$

($m > 1$, any n, positive or negative)

4.2.3 For $m,n \neq -1$,

$$\int (\ln x)^n\,dx = x(\ln x)^n - n\int (\ln x)^{n-1}\,dx$$

$$\int x^m (\ln x)^n\,dx = \frac{x^{m+1}(\ln x)^n}{m+1} - \frac{n}{m+1}\int x^m (\ln x)^{n-1}\,dx$$

4.2.4 For $n \neq 2$

$$\int \frac{dx}{x(a+bx)^{n/2}} = \frac{2}{(n-2)a(a+bx)^{(n-2)/2}} + \frac{1}{a}\int \frac{dx}{x(a+bx)^{(n-2)/2}}$$

Integrals involving $X = ax^2 + bx + c$

4.2.5 For $n \neq 1$,

$$\int \frac{dx}{X^n} = -\frac{2ax+b}{d(n-1)X^{n-1}} - \frac{2(2n-3)a}{d(n-1)}\int \frac{dx}{X^{n-1}}$$

where $d = b^2 - 4ac$ (for $n = 1$, see 3.1.14; for $n = \frac{1}{2}$, see 3.2.10)

4.2.6 For $m \neq -1$, $k = 2n - m - 1$

$$\int \frac{x^m dx}{X^n} = -\frac{x^{m-1}}{kaX^{n-1}} + \frac{(m-1)c}{ka}\int \frac{x^{m-2}dx}{X^n} - \frac{(n-m)b}{ka}\int \frac{x^{m-1}dx}{X^n}, \quad k \neq 0$$

$$= \frac{1}{a}\int \frac{x^{2n-3}dx}{X^{n-1}} - \frac{c}{a}\int \frac{x^{2n-3}dx}{X^n} - \frac{b}{a}\int \frac{x^{2n-2}dx}{X^n}, \quad k = 0$$

4.2.7 $$\int \frac{dx}{xX^n} = \frac{1}{2c(n-1)X^{n-1}} - \frac{b}{2c}\int \frac{dx}{X^n} + \frac{1}{c}\int \frac{dx}{xX^{n-1}}$$

4.2.8 $$\int X^n dx = \frac{(2ax+b)X^n}{2(2n+1)a} - \frac{nd}{2(2n+1)a}\int X^{n-1}dx \qquad (d = b^2 - 4ac)$$

(for $n = \frac{1}{2}$, see 3.2.11)

4.3 Definite integrals

4.3.1 Wallis' formula

For positive integers n,

$$\int_0^{\frac{\pi}{2}} \sin^n x \, dx = \int_0^{\frac{\pi}{2}} \cos^n x \, dx$$

$$= \frac{(n-1)(n-3)\ldots 3.1}{n(n-2)\ldots 4.2}\,\frac{\pi}{2}, \qquad n \text{ even}$$

$$= \frac{(n-1)(n-3)\ldots 4.2}{n(n-2)\ldots 3.1}, \qquad n \text{ odd}, > 1$$

For non-integral n, see 4.4.3.

4.3.2 For positive integers m,n

$$\int_0^{\frac{\pi}{2}} \sin^m x \cos^n x \, dx = \frac{(m-1)(m-3)(m-5)\ldots(n-1)(n-3)(n-5)\ldots}{(m+n)(m+n-2)(m+n-4)\ldots}\,k$$

where $k = \pi/2$ if m and n are both even
$= 1$ otherwise

For non-integral m and n, see 4.4.4.

4.3.3 For positive integers m and n,

$$\int_0^{\pi} \sin mx \sin nx \, dx = 0 , \quad m \neq n$$
$$= \pi/2, \quad m = n$$

$$\int_0^{\pi} \cos mx \cos nx \, dx = 0 , \quad m \neq n$$
$$= \pi/2, \quad m = n$$

$$\int_0^{\pi} \sin mx \cos nx \, dx = 0 , \quad m = n$$
$$= 0 , \quad m \neq n, \; m + n \text{ even}$$
$$= 2m/(m^2 - n^2), \quad m \neq n, \; m + n \text{ odd}$$

4.4 The Gamma Function

4.4.1 Definition

$$\left.\begin{aligned}\Gamma(n) &= \int_0^{\infty} x^{n-1} e^{-x} \, dx \\ &= \int_0^1 \left(\ln \frac{1}{x}\right)^{n-1} dx,\end{aligned}\right\} \text{ any } n > 0$$

4.4.2 Properties

$\Gamma(n+1) = n\Gamma(n)$ so for n integer > 0, $\Gamma(n+1) = n!$

$\Gamma(n)\Gamma(1-n) = \pi/\sin n\pi$, n not an integer

$\Gamma(\frac{1}{2}) = \sqrt{\pi}$

4.4.3 For any $n > -1$

$$\int_0^{\frac{\pi}{2}} \sin^n x \, dx = \int_0^{\frac{\pi}{2}} \cos^n x \, dx = \frac{\Gamma[(n+1)/2]}{\Gamma[(n+2)/2]} \cdot \frac{\sqrt{\pi}}{2}$$

For integral n, see 4.3.1.

4.4.4 For any $m > -1$, $n > -1$

$$\int_0^{\frac{\pi}{2}} \sin^m x \cos^n x \, dx = \frac{\Gamma[(m+1)/2]\,\Gamma[(n+1)/2]}{2\Gamma[\frac{1}{2}(m+n) + 1]}$$

For positive integral m, n see 4.3.2.

4.4.5 For $n > -1$, $a > 0$

$$\int_0^{\infty} x^n e^{-a^2x^2} dx = \frac{\Gamma[(n+1)/2]}{2a^{n+1}}$$

4.4.6 For $n > -1$, $m > 0$, $a > 0$

$$\int_0^{\infty} x^n e^{-(ax)^m} dx = \frac{\Gamma[(n+1)/m]}{ma^{n+1}}$$

4.4.7 For $m > 0$, $n > 0$

$$\int_0^1 x^{m-1}\left(\ln\frac{1}{x}\right)^{n-1}dx = \frac{\Gamma(n)}{m^n}$$

4.5 The Beta function

$$\beta(m,n) = \int_0^1 x^{m-1}(1-x)^{n-1}dx = \beta(n,m), \quad m > 0,\ n > 0$$

$$= 2\int_0^{\frac{\pi}{2}} \sin^{2m-1}\theta\ \cos^{2n-1}\theta\ d\theta = \frac{\Gamma(m)\Gamma(n)}{\Gamma(m+n)}$$

4.6 Differentiation of a definite integral (Leibnitz)

If $g(y) = \int_{h(y)}^{k(y)} f(x,y)dx$

then $\frac{dg}{dy} = \int_h^k \frac{\partial f}{\partial y}dx + f(k,y)\frac{dk}{dy} - f(h,y)\frac{dh}{dy}$

4.7 Fourier series and transforms

4.7.1 Full range Fourier series

For $f(x)$ defined on $-\ell \leqslant x \leqslant \ell$

$$f(x) \sim \tfrac{1}{2}a_0 + \sum_{n=1}^{\infty}\left[a_n \cos\frac{n\pi x}{\ell} + b_n \sin\frac{n\pi x}{\ell}\right]$$

[$\sim$ to be read as 'generates (the Fourier series)']

where

$$a_n = \frac{1}{\ell}\int_{-\ell}^{\ell} f(t)\cos\frac{n\pi t}{\ell}dt \text{ and } b_n = \frac{1}{\ell}\int_{-\ell}^{\ell} f(t)\sin\frac{n\pi t}{\ell}dt$$

4.7.2 The half-range Fourier cosine series for $f(x)$ defined on $0 \leqslant x \leqslant \ell$

$$f(x) \sim \tfrac{1}{2}A_0 + \sum_{n=1}^{\infty} A_n \cos\frac{n\pi x}{\ell} \quad \text{with} \quad A_n = \frac{2}{\ell}\int_0^{\ell} f(t)\cos\frac{n\pi t}{\ell}dt$$

4.7.3 The half-range Fourier sine series for $f(x)$ defined on $0 \leqslant x \leqslant \ell$

$$f(x) \sim \sum_{n=1}^{\infty} B_n \sin\frac{n\pi x}{\ell} \quad \text{with} \quad B_n = \frac{2}{\ell}\int_0^{\ell} f(t)\sin\frac{n\pi t}{\ell}dt$$

4.7.4 The exponential form of Fourier series for $f(x)$ defined on $-\ell \leqslant x \leqslant \ell$

$$f(x) \sim \sum_{n=-\infty}^{\infty} C_n \exp\left(\frac{in\pi x}{\ell}\right) \quad \text{where} \quad C_n = \frac{1}{2\ell}\int_{-\ell}^{\ell} f(t)\exp\left[-\frac{in\pi t}{\ell}\right]dt$$

4.7.5 Examples

Generating Function	Fourier Series
$f(x) = -1, \; -\ell \leqslant x < 0$ $\quad = 1, \; 0 \leqslant x \leqslant \ell$	$\frac{4}{\pi}\left[\sin\frac{\pi x}{\ell} + \frac{1}{3}\sin\frac{3\pi x}{\ell} + \frac{1}{5}\sin\frac{5\pi x}{\ell} + \ldots\right]$
$f(x) = a\left(1+\frac{2x}{\ell}\right), \; -\ell \leqslant x < 0$ $\quad = a\left(1-\frac{2x}{\ell}\right), \; 0 \leqslant x \leqslant \ell$	$\frac{8a}{\pi^2}\left[\cos\frac{\pi x}{\ell} + \frac{1}{3^2}\cos\frac{3\pi x}{\ell} + \frac{1}{5^2}\cos\frac{5\pi x}{\ell} + \ldots\right]$
$f(x) = \frac{ax}{\ell}, \; -\ell \leqslant x \leqslant \ell$	$\frac{2a}{\pi}\left[\sin\frac{\pi x}{\ell} - \frac{1}{2}\sin\frac{2\pi x}{\ell} + \frac{1}{3}\sin\frac{3\pi x}{\ell} - \ldots\right]$
$f(x) = \sin\frac{\pi x}{\ell}, \; 0 \leqslant x \leqslant \ell$	$\frac{2}{\pi} - \frac{4}{\pi}\left[\frac{\cos\frac{2\pi x}{\ell}}{1.3} + \frac{\cos\frac{4\pi x}{\ell}}{3.5} + \frac{\cos\frac{6\pi x}{\ell}}{5.7} + \ldots\right]$
$f(x) = \sin\frac{\pi x}{\ell}, \; 0 \leqslant x < \ell$ $\quad = 0, \; \ell \leqslant x \leqslant 2\ell$	$\frac{1}{\pi} + \frac{1}{2}\sin\frac{\pi x}{\ell} - \frac{2}{\pi}\left[\frac{\cos\frac{2\pi x}{\ell}}{1.3} + \frac{\cos\frac{4\pi x}{\ell}}{3.5} + \ldots\right]$

Graph of series

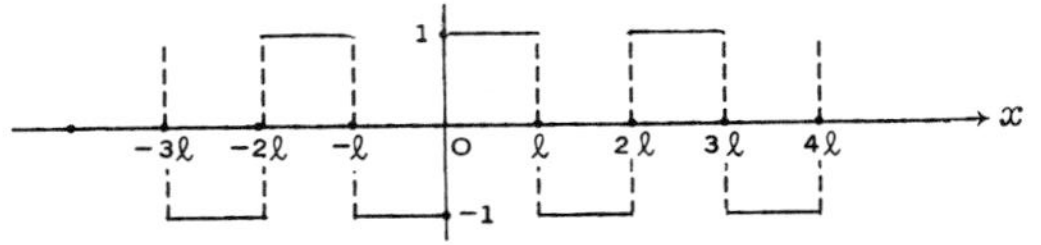

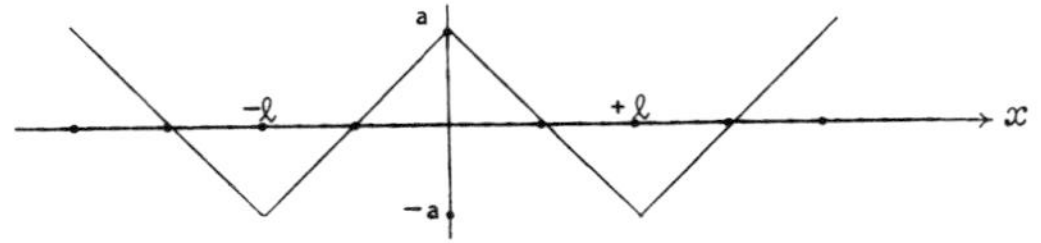

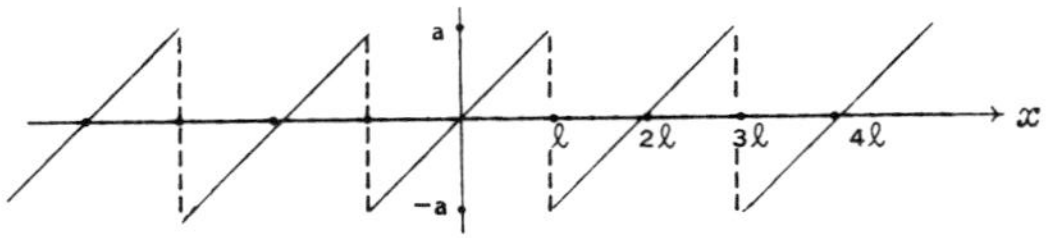

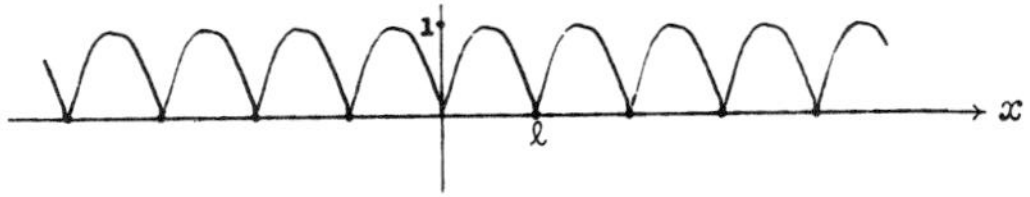

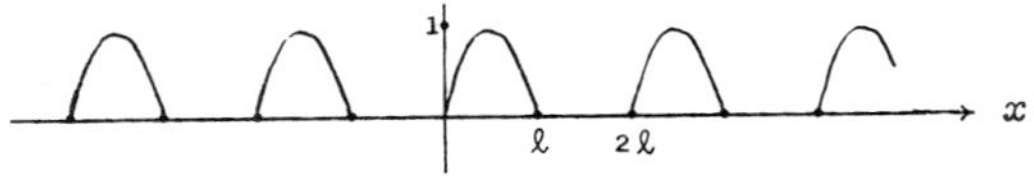

4.7.6 Odd and even functions

When $f(x)$ is *even*, i.e. $f(x) = f(-x)$ then

$$a_n = \frac{2}{\ell}\int_0^{\ell} f(t)\cos\frac{n\pi t}{\ell}dt, \quad b_n = 0$$

When $f(x)$ is *odd*, i.e. $f(x) = -f(-x)$ then

$$a_n = 0, \quad b_n = \frac{2}{\ell}\int_0^{\ell} f(t)\sin\frac{n\pi t}{\ell}dt$$

4.7.7 Two useful integrals

$$\int t^m \cos\frac{t}{a}dt = at^m \sin\frac{t}{a} - am\int t^{m-1}\sin\frac{t}{a}dt$$

$$\int t^m \sin\frac{t}{a}dt = -at^m \cos\frac{t}{a} + am\int t^{m-1}\cos\frac{t}{a}dt, \quad m = 1,2,3,\ldots$$

For Fourier series use $a = \ell/n\pi$.

4.7.8 Fourier (Integral) transforms

.1 A function $f(t)$ and its Fourier transform, written $\bar{f}(\omega)$ or $F\{f(t)\}$, are related by the integrals

$$\bar{f}(\omega) = \int_{-\infty}^{\infty} e^{-i\omega t} f(t)dt, \quad f(t) = \frac{1}{2\pi}\int_{-\infty}^{\infty} e^{i\omega t}\bar{f}(\omega)d\omega$$

(Note: Slightly different forms are found.)

.2 Sine transform

$$\bar{f}_s(\omega) = \int_0^{\infty} f(t)\sin\omega t\, dt, \quad f(t) = \frac{2}{\pi}\int_0^{\infty}\bar{f}_s(\omega)\sin\omega t\, d\omega$$

.3 Cosine transform

$$\bar{f}_c(\omega) = \int_0^{\infty} f(t)\cos\omega t\, dt, \quad f(t) = \frac{2}{\pi}\int_0^{\infty}\bar{f}_c(\omega)\cos\omega t\, d\omega$$

.4 Discrete Fourier transform (DFT)

$$\left.\begin{aligned} \bar{x}_\ell &= \sum_{k=0}^{n-1} x_k\, \omega^{\ell k} \\ x_k &= \frac{1}{n}\sum_{\ell=0}^{n-1} \bar{x}_\ell\, \omega^{-\ell k} \end{aligned}\right\} \quad \omega = e^{-i 2\pi/n}$$

5. ORDINARY DIFFERENTIAL EQUATIONS

5.1 Order and degree

The *order* of a differential equation is the order of the highest derivative which occurs. The *degree* of the equation is the degree of the highest derivative, after the equation has been made rational so far as derivatives are concerned.

5.2 Equations of first order and first degree

$$f(x,y,y') = 0$$

5.2.1 Variables separable

$$g(x) + h(y)y' = 0$$

has solution

$$\int g(x)dx + \int h(y)dy = \text{constant} .$$

5.2.2 Homogeneous

A *homogeneous* function of x and y having degree n satisfies the relation $f(kx,ky) = k^n f(x,y)$. If g and h are two homogeneous functions having the same degree the equation

$$g(x,y) + h(x,y)y' = 0$$

is called homogeneous.

The substitution $y = xv(x)$, $y' = v + xv'$ reduces the equation to one of type 5.2.1 in $v(x)$.

5.2.3 Linear coefficients

$$(a_1 x + b_1 y + c_1) + (a_2 x + b_2 y + c_2)y' = 0$$

Let the solution of the simultaneous equations

$$a_1 x + b_1 y + c_1 = 0, \quad a_2 x + b_2 y + c_2 = 0$$

be (h,k). The substitution $x = X + h$, $y = Y + k$ reduces the equation to type (5.2.2).

If $a_1 b_2 = a_2 b_1$, h and k do not exist; in this case, use 5.2.1 if relevant. Otherwise, the substitution $z = a_1 x + b_1 y$ reduces the equation to one of type (5.2.1) in $z(x)$.

5.2.4 Exact

The equation

$$g(x,y) + h(x,y)y' = 0$$

is *exact* if

$$\frac{\partial g}{\partial y} = \frac{\partial h}{\partial x} ,$$

and has solution

$$u(x,y) = \text{constant},$$

where $\dfrac{\partial u}{\partial x} = g(x,y)$, $\dfrac{\partial u}{\partial y} = h(x,y)$.

5.2.5 Linear

$$y' + P(x)y = Q(x)$$

Multiply by the *integrating factor*

$$R(x) = \exp\left(\int P(x)dx\right)$$

to obtain $yR(x) = \displaystyle\int R(x)Q(x)dx$.

5.2.6 Bernoulli equation

$$y' + P(x)y = Q(x)y^n \qquad n \neq 0,1.$$

The substitution $z = y^{1-n}$ reduces this to type 5.2.5.

5.2.7 Riccati equation

$$y' = g(x)y^2 + h(x)y + k(x)$$

(i) A solution is $y(x) = y_2(x)/y_1(x)$ where

$$y_1' = -\tfrac{1}{2}h(x)y_1 - g(x)y_2$$

$$y_2' = k(x)y_1 + \tfrac{1}{2}h(x)y_2$$

(ii) The substitution $y(x) = -w'(x)/\left[g(x)w(x)\right]$ reduces the equation to a second order *linear* equation in $w(x)$.

5.3 Equations of first order, and degree greater than one

In the following let p denote $\dfrac{dy}{dx}$

5.3.1 Solvable for p

By factorization, if possible, an equation of n-th order can be reduced to n first-order, first degree equations

i.e. $$(p - f_1)(p - f_2) \ldots (p - f_n) = 0$$

where the f's are functions of x and y.

5.3.2 Solvable for y

$$y = f(x,p)$$

Differentiate with respect to x to obtain a first order equation in p and x.

5.3.3 Solvable for x

$$x = f(y,p)$$

Differentiate with respect to y and write $dx/dy = 1/p$ to obtain a first order equation in p and y.

5.4 Equations of second order

5.4.1 y absent

Write p for y', p' for y'' to obtain a first order equation in p and x.

5.4.2 x absent

Write p for y', pdp/dy for y'' to obtain a first order equation in p and y.

5.5 Linear equations with constant coefficients

$$\frac{d^n y}{dx^n} + a_1 \frac{d^{n-1}y}{dx^{n-1}} + \ldots + a_{n-1}\frac{dy}{dx} + a_n y = f(x) \qquad 5.5\ (1)$$

where the a's are all real constants.

When $f(x) \equiv 0$ in 5.5(1), the equation is said to be *homogeneous*. The general solution of 5.5(1) is

complementary function + *particular integral*

where the complementary function is the general solution of the homogeneous equation and contains n arbitrary constants, and the particular integral is a particular solution of 5.5(1), independent of arbitrary constants.

5.5.1 Complementary function

This is obtained as the sum of terms corresponding to roots of $a(\lambda) \equiv \lambda^n + a_1\lambda^{n-1} + \ldots + a_{n-1}\lambda + a_n = 0$.

Roots	Term in complementary function
α real, simple	$Ae^{\alpha x}$
β real, r-fold	$(B_1 x^{r-1} + B_2 x^{r-2} + \ldots + B_r)e^{\beta x}$
$\gamma \pm i\delta$, complex conjugate pair	$(C_1 \cos \delta x + C_2 \sin \delta x)e^{\gamma x}$
$\varepsilon \pm i\phi$ complex conjugate pair, r-fold	$e^{\varepsilon x}\left[\left(D_1 x^{r-1} + D_2 x^{r-2} + \ldots + D_r\right)\cos\phi x + \left(E_1 x^{r-1} + E_2 x^{r-2} + \ldots + E_r\right)\sin\phi x\right]$

The capital letters denote arbitrary constants.

5.5.2 Particular integrals using undetermined coefficients

Step 1. Select a form of particular integral (P.I.) according to the following rule.

When the right hand side of the equation consists of a sum of terms in the column marked $f(x)$ of the table below, the form of P.I. to be taken consists of a sum of the forms appropriate to each term separately, subject to the following:

CASE 1 The form of P.I. from the table below is used as it stands if it does not already occur in the complementary function (C.F.)

CASE 2 Where the form as taken from the table is already contained in the C.F., corresponding to an r-fold root in $a(\lambda)$, the expression on the right hand side of the table must be multiplied by x^r.

$f(x)$	Form of particular integral
$e^{kx}\sin mx$ or $e^{kx}\cos mx$ (including $k = 0$)	$e^{kx}\left(A\sin mx + B\cos mx\right)$
$e^{kx}\left(p_0 + p_1x + p_2x^2 + \ldots + p_s x^s\right) = e^{kx}p^{(s)}(x)$ (including $k = 0$)	$e^{kx}\left(P_0 + P_1x + P_2x^2 + \ldots + P_s x^s\right) = e^{kx}P^{(s)}(x)$
$p^{(s)}(x)\sin mx + q^{(t)}(x)\cos mx$	$P^{(u)}\sin mx + Q^{(u)}\cos mx$

$u = \max(s,t)$

Step 2. Determine the coefficients of the P.I. by substitution in the equation 5.5 (1) to be solved.

Example. Suppose the right hand side of the equation is $x^2 + \cos 2x$ and $a(\lambda) = (\lambda^2 + 4)^2$, so that the C.F. is $(D_1x + D_2)\cos 2x + (E_1x + E_2)\sin 2x$. The form of P.I. corresponding to x^2 is $P_0 + P_1x + P_2x^2$, which since it does not occur in the C.F., is used as it stands. The form of P.I. corresponding to $\cos 2x$ is $P\cos 2x + Q\sin 2x$, a form which occurs in the C.F. corresponding to a double root. Hence $x^2(P\cos 2x + Q\sin 2x)$ is the required form corresponding to the term $\cos 2x$. The complete form of P.I. is the sum of these, namely

$$P_0 + P_1x + P_2x^2 + x^2(P\cos 2x + Q\sin 2x)\ ,$$

where the five constants P_0, P_1, P_2, P, Q are to be determined. The following special forms are often useful:

5.5.3 Simple particular integrals

$f(x)$	Particular integral
e^{kx}, $a(k) \neq 0$	$\dfrac{e^{kx}}{a(k)}$
e^{kx}, $a(\lambda) = (\lambda - k)^r a_1(\lambda)$, $a_1(k) \neq 0$	$\dfrac{e^{kx} x^r}{a_1(k) r!}$
$\left.\begin{matrix}\cos mx \\ \sin mx\end{matrix}\right\}$	Treat as $\begin{matrix}\mathcal{R}e \\ Im\end{matrix}\left\{e^{imx}\right\}$

5.6 Euler's linear equation

$$x^n \frac{d^n y}{dx^n} + a_1 x^{n-1} \frac{d^{n-1} y}{dx^{n-1}} + \ldots + a_{n-1} x \frac{dy}{dx} + a_n y = f(x),$$

with all a's real constants.

The substitution

$$x = e^t,\ x\frac{dy}{dx} = \frac{dy}{dt}, \ldots,\ x^n \frac{d^n y}{dx^n} = \frac{d}{dt}\left(\frac{d}{dt} - 1\right)\left(\frac{d}{dt} - 2\right)\ldots\left(\frac{d}{dt} - n + 1\right)y$$

reduces the equation to one of type 5.5 in y and t.

5.7 Special equations

$$a(x)\frac{d^2 y}{dx^2} + b(x)\frac{dy}{dx} + c(x)y = 0$$

$y(x)$	$a(x)$	$b(x)$	$c(x)$
$T_n(x)$	$1 - x^2$	$-x$	n^2
$U_n(x)$	$1 - x^2$	$-3x$	$n(n + 2)$
$H_n(x)$	1	$-2x$	$2n$
$P_n(x)$	$1 - x^2$	$-2x$	$n(n + 1)$
$L_n^{\alpha}(x)$	x	$\alpha + 1 - x$	n
$C_n^{\alpha}(x)$	$1 - x^2$	$-(2\alpha + 1)x$	$n(n + 2\alpha)$
$J_n(x)$	x^2	x	$x^2 - n^2$

$J_n(x)$ is the *Bessel function* of the first kind; the other functions are named in Section 9.13.1.

6. LAPLACE AND Z TRANSFORMS

6.1 The Laplace transform $\bar{x}(s)$ *of* $x(t)$

$$\bar{x}(s) \equiv \mathcal{L}\{x(t)\} = \int_0^\infty e^{-st}\, x(t)dt$$

6.2 The Inverse Laplace transform of $\bar{x}(s)$

$$\mathcal{L}^{-1}\{\bar{x}(s)\} = \frac{1}{2\pi i}\int_{\gamma-i\infty}^{\gamma+i\infty} e^{ts}\,\bar{x}(s)ds = x(t)H(t), \text{ where } H(t) = 0,\ t < 0;\quad = 1,\ t > 0$$

The integration is to be performed along the line $s = \gamma$ in the complex s-plane where γ is such that the line $s = \gamma$ lies to the right of all singularities of $\bar{x}(s)$ but is otherwise arbitrary.

Note. Though not apparent from 6.1 it follows from 6.2 that the function transformed is actually $x(t)H(t)$, which is of course equal to $x(t)$ for $t > 0$. The importance of this is to be noticed in 6.3.9(a) where the function shifted is $x(t)H(t)$ not $x(t)$.

6.3.	General transforms	$\bar{x}(s)$	$x(t)$
1	Linearity	$a\bar{x}_1(s) + b\bar{x}_2(s)$	$ax_1(t) + bx_2(t)$
2	Change of scale	$\frac{1}{a}\bar{x}\left(\frac{s}{a}\right)$	$x(at)$
3	Differentiation and Integration	$s\bar{x} - x(0)$	$dx/dt \equiv x^{(1)}(t)$
4		$\frac{\bar{x}(s)}{s}$	$\int_0^t x(u)du$
5		$d\bar{x}/ds$	$-tx(t)$
6		$\int_s^\infty \bar{x}(u)du$	$\frac{x(t)}{t}$
7		$s^n\bar{x} - s^{n-1}x(0) - s^{n-2}x^{(1)}(0) - \ldots - x^{(n-1)}(0)$	$x^{(n)}(t)$
8	1st Shifting Theorem	$\bar{x}(s-a)$ $\quad \mathcal{Re}(s) > a$	$e^{at}x(t)$
9	2nd Shifting Theorem (a)	$e^{-as}\bar{x}(s)$, $a > 0$	$x(t-a)H(t-a)$
	(b)	$e^{-as}\mathcal{L}\{x(t+a)\}$, $a > 0$	$x(t)H(t-a)$
10	Periodic function of period T	$\frac{1}{1-e^{-sT}}\int_0^T e^{-st}\,x(t)dt$	$x(t) = x(t+T)$
11	Convolution Theorem	$\bar{x}(s)\bar{y}(s)$	$\int_0^t x(u)y(t-u)du$

Note: The above table is constructed to exhibit the duality between operations on function and transform (e.g., 6.3.3 & 6.3.5; 6.3.4 & 6.3.6)

6.4 Particular transform pairs

6.4.	$\bar{x}(s)$	$x(t)$
1	0	$N(t)$ null function
2	e^{-as}	$\delta(t-a)$ delta function
3	$\frac{1}{s}$	1 [or $H(t)$]
4	$\frac{e^{-as}}{s}$	$H(t-a)$ (see 6.3.9)
5	$\frac{n!}{s^{n+1}}$	t^n $(n=1,2,3\ldots)$
6	$\frac{\Gamma(k+1)}{s^{k+1}}$	t^k $\mathcal{Re}(k) > -1$
7	$\frac{1}{s-a}$	e^{at}
8	$\frac{a}{s^2+a^2}$	$\sin at$
9	$\frac{s}{s^2+a^2}$	$\cos at$
10	$\frac{s\sin\phi + a\cos\phi}{s^2+a^2}$	$\sin(at+\phi)$
11	$\frac{a}{s^2-a^2}$	$\sinh at$
12	$\frac{s}{s^2-a^2}$	$\cosh at$
13	$\frac{1}{(s^2+a^2)^2}$	$(\sin at - at\cos at)/2a^3$
14	$\frac{1}{(s^2-a^2)^2}$	$(at\cosh at - \sinh at)/2a^3$
15	$\frac{s}{(s^2+a^2)^2}$	$(t\sin at)/2a$
16	$\frac{s}{(s^2-a^2)^2}$	$(t\sinh at)/2a$
17	$\frac{s^2-a^2}{(s^2+a^2)^2}$	$t\cos at$
18	$\frac{s^2+a^2}{(s^2-a^2)^2}$	$t\cosh at$
19	$\frac{s^2}{(s^2+a^2)^2}$	$(\sin at + at\cos at)/2a$
20	$\frac{s^2}{(s^2-a^2)^2}$	$(\sinh at + at\cosh at)/2a$
21	$\frac{s^3}{(s^2+a^2)^2}$	$\cos at - \frac{1}{2}at\sin at$
22	$\frac{s^3}{(s^2-a^2)^2}$	$\cosh at + \frac{1}{2}at\sinh at$
23	$\frac{1}{(s^2+a^2)^3}$	$[(3-a^2t^2)\sin at - 3at\cos at]/8a^5$

6.4.	Particular transform pairs (cont...)	
	$\bar{x}(s)$	$x(t)$
24	$\dfrac{1}{(s^2 - a^2)^3}$	$[(3 + a^2t^2)\sinh at - 3at\cosh at]/8a^5$
25	$\dfrac{s^2}{(s^2 + a^2)^3}$	$[(1 + a^2t^2)\sin at - at\cos at]/8a^3$
26	$\dfrac{s^2}{(s^2 - a^2)^3}$	$[at\cosh at + (a^2t^2 - 1)\sinh at]/8a^3$
27	$\dfrac{s^4}{(s^2 + a^2)^3}$	$[(3 - a^2t^2)\sin at + 5at\cos at]/8a$
28	$\dfrac{s^4}{(s^2 - a^2)^3}$	$[(3 - a^2t^2)\sinh at + 5at\cosh at]/8a$
29	$\dfrac{1}{s^3 + a^3}$	$e^{\frac{1}{2}at}\left[\sqrt{3}\sin\frac{\sqrt{3}}{2}at - \cos\frac{\sqrt{3}}{2}at + e^{-3at/2}\right]/3a^2$
30	$\dfrac{s^2}{s^3 + a^3}$	$\left[e^{-at} + 2e^{\frac{1}{2}at}\cos\frac{\sqrt{3}}{2}at\right]/3$
31	$\dfrac{1, s^2}{s^3 - a^3}$	Use 29, 30 with a replaced by $-a$
32	$\dfrac{1}{s^4 + 4a^4}$	$(\sin at\cosh at - \cos at\sinh at)/4a^3$
33	$\dfrac{1}{s^4 - a^4}$	$(\sinh at - \sin at)/2a^3$
34	$\dfrac{s^2}{s^4 + 4a^4}$	$(\sin at\cosh at + \cos at\sinh at)/2a$
35	$\dfrac{s^2}{s^4 - a^4}$	$(\sinh at + \sin at)/2a$
36	$\dfrac{1}{(s - a)(s - b)}$	$(e^{bt} - e^{at})/(b - a)$ $(a \neq b)$
37	$\dfrac{1}{(s + a)(s^2 + b^2)}$	$(be^{-at} - b\cos bt + a\sin bt)/b(a^2 + b^2)$
38	$\dfrac{1}{s}\tanh\dfrac{as}{2}$	Rectangular Wave function 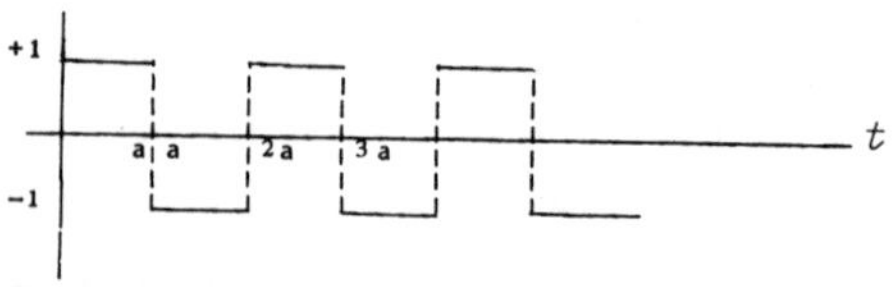
39	$\dfrac{1}{as^2}\tanh\dfrac{as}{2}$	Triangular Wave function 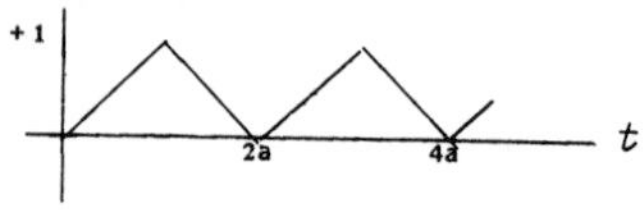

6.4.	Particular transform pairs (cont...)	
	$\bar{x}(s)$	$x(t)$
40	$\dfrac{1}{as^2} - \dfrac{e^{-as}}{s(1-e^{-as})}$	Saw tooth wave function 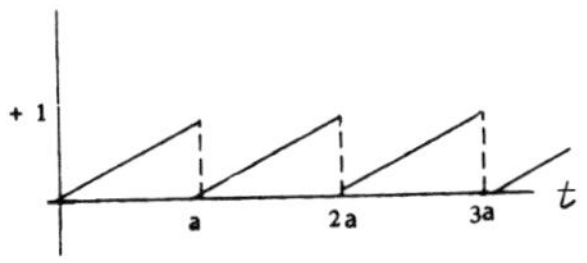
41	$\dfrac{\pi a}{a^2 s^2 + \pi^2} \coth\left(\dfrac{as}{2}\right)$	Rectified sine wave function 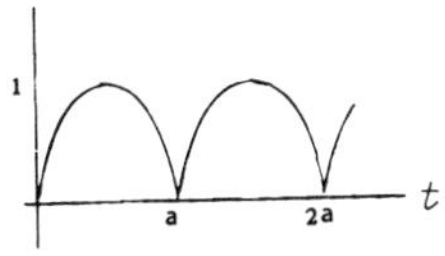 $x(t) = \left\lvert \sin \dfrac{\pi t}{a} \right\rvert$
42	$\dfrac{\pi a}{(a^2 s^2 + \pi^2)(1 - e^{-as})}$	Half-rectified sine wave function 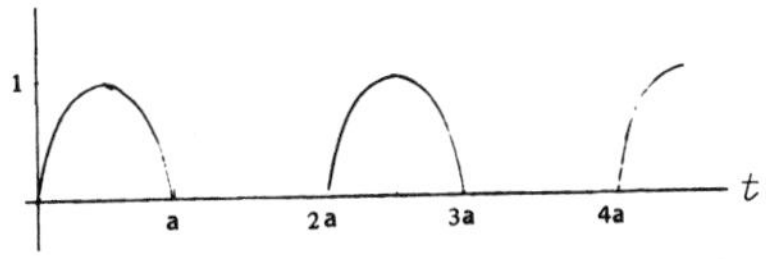
43	$\dfrac{1}{s(1-e^{-s})}$	Staircase function 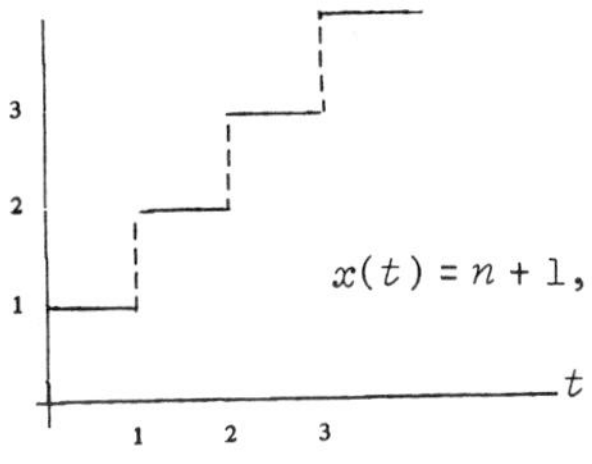 $x(t) = n + 1, \quad n < t < n + 1$
44	$\dfrac{\left[\sqrt{(s^2+1)} - s\right]^n}{\sqrt{(s^2+1)}}$	$J_n(t)$ $\qquad n > -1$
45	$\dfrac{\left[s - \sqrt{(s^2-1)}\right]^n}{\sqrt{(s^2-1)}}$	$I_n(t)$ $\qquad n > -1$
46	$-\dfrac{\ln s}{s}$	$\gamma + \ln t,$ $\qquad \gamma = 0{\cdot}577216$
47	$\ln\left(\dfrac{s+a}{s+b}\right)$	$\dfrac{e^{-bt} - e^{-at}}{t}$

6.5 The z-transform $\tilde{x}(z)$ of $x(n)$, $n = 0,1,2,\ldots$

$$\tilde{x}(z) = Z\{x(n)\} = \sum_{n=0}^{\infty} x(n)z^{-n}$$

6.6 The inverse z-transform of $\tilde{x}(z)$

$$Z^{-1}\{\tilde{x}(z)\} = \frac{1}{2\pi i}\oint_{\Gamma} z^{n-1}\tilde{x}(z)dz = x(n)H(n)$$

The integration is to be performed in the anticlockwise direction around the circle Γ in the complex z-plane, where Γ is such that it encloses all the singularities of $\tilde{x}(z)$.

6.7 General transforms

6.7.		$\tilde{x}(z)$	$x(n)$
1	Linearity	$a\tilde{x}_1(z) + b\tilde{x}_2(z)$	$ax_1(n) + bx_2(n)$
2	Change of scale	$\tilde{x}\left(\frac{z}{a}\right)$	$a^n x(n)$
3		$z\tilde{x} - zx(0)$	$x(n + 1)$
4		$\frac{z\tilde{x}}{z - 1}$	$\sum_{i=0}^{n} x(i)$
5		$z(d\tilde{x}/dz)$	$- nx(n)$
6		$\int_z^{\infty} \frac{\tilde{x}(u)}{u}\,du + \lim_{n\to 0} \frac{x(n)}{n}$	$\frac{x(n)}{n}$
7	Left shifting	$z^k\tilde{x} - z^k x(0) - z^{k-1}x(1) - \ldots - z^2x(k - 2) - zx(k - 1)$	$x(n + k)$, $k = 1,2,3,\ldots$
8	Right shifting	$z^{-k}\tilde{x}(z)$, $k = 1,2,3,\ldots$	$x(n - k)H(n - k)$
9	Periodic sequence	$\frac{z^N}{z^N - 1}\sum_{n=0}^{N-1} x(n)z^{-n}$	$x(n) = x(n + N)$
10	Convolution	$\tilde{x}(z)\tilde{y}(z)$	$\sum_{i=0}^{n} x(i)y(n - i)$

Note: The above table is constructed so as to exhibit the parallels with Table 6.3 for the Laplace transform.

6.8 Particular transform pairs

6.8.	$\tilde{x}(z)$	$x(n)$
1	1	$\delta(n)$
2	z^{-k}	$\delta(n-k)\begin{cases}=1, & n=k\\=0, & \text{otherwise}\end{cases}$
3	$\dfrac{z^{-k+1}}{z-1}$	$H(n-k)\begin{cases}=1, & n\geqslant k\\=0, & \text{otherwise}\end{cases}$
4	$\dfrac{z}{(z-1)^2}$	n
5	$\dfrac{z(z+1)}{(z-1)^3}$	n^2
6	$\dfrac{z(z^2+4z+1)}{(z-1)^4}$	n^3
7	$\dfrac{z(z^3+11z^2+11z+1)}{(z-1)^5}$	n^4
8	$(-1)^k\left(z\dfrac{d}{dz}\right)^k\left(\dfrac{z}{z-1}\right)$	$n^k,\ k=1,2,3,\ldots$
9	$\dfrac{z}{z-a}$	a^n
10	$\dfrac{az}{(z-a)^2}$	na^n
11	$\left(\dfrac{a}{z}\right)^j\left(\dfrac{z}{z-a}\right)^{k+1}$	$\begin{pmatrix}n+k-j\\k\end{pmatrix}a^n$ $k=1,2,3,\ldots;\ j\leqslant k$
12	$\dfrac{(a+bz)^k}{z^k}$	$\begin{pmatrix}k\\n\end{pmatrix}a^n b^{k-n},\ n\leqslant k$
13	$\dfrac{z\sin w}{z^2-2z\cos w+1}$	$\sin wn$
14	$\dfrac{z(z-\cos w)}{z^2-2z\cos w+1}$	$\cos wn$
15	$\dfrac{z\sinh w}{z^2-2z\cosh w+1}$	$\sinh wn$
16	$\dfrac{z(z-\cosh w)}{z^2-2z\cosh w+1}$	$\cosh wn$
17	$\ell n\dfrac{z}{z-a}$	$a^n/n,\ n>0;\ 0,\ n=0$
18	$\exp(a/z)$	$a^n/n!$
19	$\dfrac{z}{(z-a)(z-b)}$	$(b^n-a^n)/(b-a)\quad(a\neq b)$

7. VECTORS

7.1 $\underline{a} = |\underline{a}|\,\hat{\underline{a}}$

7.1.1 $|\underline{a}|$ the modulus of $\underline{a}$ = the magnitude (length) of the vector $\underline{a}$. (See 7.4.2).

7.1.2 $\hat{\underline{a}}$ = a vector of unit length (a *unit vector*) in the direction of the vector $\underline{a}$.

7.1.3 Null vector: a vector of zero modulus.

7.2 $\underline{a} = a_1\underline{i} + a_2\underline{j} + a_3\underline{k}$

7.2.1 $\underline{i}, \underline{j}$ and $\underline{k}$ are unit vectors along the axes of the rectangular cartesian system (x,y,z).

7.2.2 a_1, a_2, a_3 are the *co-ordinates* of the end point of $\underline{a}$ when the initial point of $\underline{a}$ is at the origin of the system (x,y,z).

7.2.3 In particular $\underline{r} = x\underline{i} + y\underline{j} + z\underline{k}$ is called the *position vector* of the point (x,y,z).

7.2.4 $c\underline{a} = ca_1\underline{i} + ca_2\underline{j} + ca_3\underline{k}$, where c is a scalar.

7.2.5 In the case of rectangular systems only, these coordinates are equal to the *components of the vector* in the associated directions. (See 7.4.4).

7.3 Scalar (or dot) Product of two Vectors

$\underline{a}.\underline{b} = |\underline{a}||\underline{b}|\cos\theta, \quad 0 \leqslant \theta \leqslant \pi$ where θ is the angle between $\underline{a}$ and $\underline{b}$.

Note that $\underline{a}.\underline{b}$ is a scalar quantity and that

$$\underline{i}.\underline{i} = \underline{j}.\underline{j} = \underline{k}.\underline{k} = 1, \qquad \underline{i}.\underline{j} = \underline{j}.\underline{k} = \underline{k}.\underline{i} = 0 .$$

7.4 Properties of scalar product

If $\underline{a} = a_1\underline{i} + a_2\underline{j} + a_3\underline{k}$, $\underline{b} = b_1\underline{i} + b_2\underline{j} + b_3\underline{k}$

7.4.1 $\underline{a}.\underline{b} = a_1b_1 + a_2b_2 + a_3b_3$

7.4.2 $\underline{a}.\underline{a} = |\underline{a}|^2 = a_1^2 + a_2^2 + a_3^2$

7.4.3 The component of $\underline{a}$ in the direction of $\underline{b}$ is $|\underline{a}|\cos\theta = \underline{a}.\hat{\underline{b}}$

7.4.4 Since $\underline{a}.\underline{i} = a_1$, $\underline{a}.\underline{j} = a_2$, $\underline{a}.\underline{k} = a_3$
the coordinates of $\underline{a}$ in a rectangular cartesian system are also its components in the directions of the axes.

7.4.5 $\underline{a} = (\underline{a}.\underline{i})\underline{i} + (\underline{a}.\underline{j})\underline{j} + (\underline{a}.\underline{k})\underline{k}$

7.4.6 If $\underline{a}.\underline{b} = 0$ and $\underline{a}$ and $\underline{b}$ are not null vectors, then $\underline{a}$ is perpendicular to $\underline{b}$.

7.5 The vector (or cross) Product of two vectors

$\underline{a} \times \underline{b} = |\underline{a}||\underline{b}|\sin\theta\, \hat{\underline{n}}$, $0 \leqslant \theta \leqslant \pi$ where θ is the angle between $\underline{a}$ and $\underline{b}$ and where $\hat{\underline{n}}$ is a unit vector perpendicular to the plane of $\underline{a}$ and $\underline{b}$ and such that $\underline{a}$, $\underline{b}$ and $\hat{\underline{n}}$ form a right-handed system.

In particular

$$\underline{i} \times \underline{i} = \underline{j} \times \underline{j} = \underline{k} \times \underline{k} = 0; \quad \underline{i} \times \underline{j} = \underline{k},\ \underline{j} \times \underline{k} = \underline{i},\ \underline{k} \times \underline{i} = \underline{j}.$$

The notation $\underline{c} = \underline{a}_{\wedge}\underline{b}$ (read '$\underline{a}$ vec $\underline{b}$') is often used.

Properties of vector product

7.5.1 $\underline{a} \times \underline{b} = -\underline{b} \times \underline{a}$

7.5.2 If $\underline{a} = a_1\underline{i} + a_2\underline{j} + a_3\underline{k}$, $\underline{b} = b_1\underline{i} + b_2\underline{j} + b_3\underline{k}$

$$\underline{a} \times \underline{b} = \begin{vmatrix} \underline{i} & \underline{j} & \underline{k} \\ a_1 & a_2 & a_3 \\ b_1 & b_2 & b_3 \end{vmatrix}$$

7.5.3 $|\underline{a} \times \underline{b}| = |\underline{a}||\underline{b}|\sin\theta$ is the area of a parallelogram with sides $\underline{a}$ and $\underline{b}$.

7.5.4 If $\underline{a} \times \underline{b} = 0$, and $\underline{a}$ and $\underline{b}$ are not null vectors, then $\underline{a}$ and $\underline{b}$ are parallel.

7.6 Scalar Triple Product

$[\underline{abc}] = \underline{a}.(\underline{b} \times \underline{c}) = (\underline{a} \times \underline{b}).\underline{c}$ = Volume of a parallelepiped with edges $\underline{a}$, $\underline{b}$ and $\underline{c}$.

7.6.1 $[\underline{abc}] = [\underline{bca}] = [\underline{cab}] = -[\underline{acb}] = -[\underline{cba}] = -[\underline{bac}]$

7.6.2 In cartesian coordinates

$$[\underline{a}\ \underline{b}\ \underline{c}] = \begin{vmatrix} a_1 & a_2 & a_3 \\ b_1 & b_2 & b_3 \\ c_1 & c_2 & c_3 \end{vmatrix}$$

7.6.3 $[\underline{a}\ \underline{b}\ \underline{c}] = 0$, if any two vectors are equal or proportional.

7.7 Vector Triple Product

$$\underline{a} \times (\underline{b} \times \underline{c}) = (\underline{a}.\underline{c})\underline{b} - (\underline{a}.\underline{b})\underline{c}.$$

7.7.1 $\underline{a} \times (\underline{b} \times \underline{c}) \neq (\underline{a} \times \underline{b}) \times \underline{c}$. i.e. the vector product is not associative.

7.8 Other Products

7.8.1 $(\underline{a} \times \underline{b}).(\underline{c} \times \underline{d}) = (\underline{a}.\underline{c})(\underline{b}.\underline{d}) - (\underline{a}.\underline{d})(\underline{b}.\underline{c}) = \begin{vmatrix} \underline{a}.\underline{c} & \underline{a}.\underline{d} \\ \underline{b}.\underline{c} & \underline{b}.\underline{d} \end{vmatrix}$

7.8.2 $(\underline{a} \times \underline{b}) \times (\underline{c} \times \underline{d}) = [\underline{acd}]\underline{b} - [\underline{bcd}]\underline{a} = [\underline{abd}]\underline{c} - [\underline{abc}]\underline{d}$

7.9 Frenet-Serret Formulae

$$\frac{d\hat{\underline{t}}}{ds} = \kappa\,\hat{\underline{n}}\,, \qquad \frac{d\hat{\underline{n}}}{ds} = \tau\,\hat{\underline{b}} - \kappa\,\hat{\underline{t}}\,, \qquad \frac{d\hat{\underline{b}}}{ds} = -\tau\,\hat{\underline{n}}$$

where $\hat{\underline{t}}$, $\hat{\underline{n}}$, $\hat{\underline{b}}$ are unit vectors in the directions of the tangent, principal normal, and binormal respectively to a curve. κ is called the *curvature* and τ the *torsion* of the curve, s is the distance along the curve.

Vector Operators

7.10 The Vector Differential Operator ∇

$$\nabla \equiv \underline{i}\frac{\partial}{\partial x} + \underline{j}\frac{\partial}{\partial y} + \underline{k}\frac{\partial}{\partial z} \equiv \frac{\partial}{\partial x}\underline{i} + \frac{\partial}{\partial y}\underline{j} + \frac{\partial}{\partial z}\underline{k}$$

pronounced 'grad', 'div' or 'nabla'.

7.11 The Gradient of a Scalar Point Function $\phi(x,y,z)$

$$\text{grad}\ \phi = \underline{i}\frac{\partial\phi}{\partial x} + \underline{j}\frac{\partial\phi}{\partial y} + \underline{k}\frac{\partial\phi}{\partial z} = \nabla\phi$$

$\nabla\phi$ gives the magnitude and direction of the maximum rate of change of ϕ.

7.12 The Divergence of a Vector Point Function $\underline{F}(x,y,z) = F_1\underline{i} + F_2\underline{j} + F_3\underline{k}$

$$\text{div}\ \underline{F} = \frac{\partial F_1}{\partial x} + \frac{\partial F_2}{\partial y} + \frac{\partial F_3}{\partial z} = \underline{i}.\frac{\partial \underline{F}}{\partial x} + \underline{j}.\frac{\partial \underline{F}}{\partial y} + \underline{k}.\frac{\partial \underline{F}}{\partial z} = \nabla.\underline{F}$$

7.13 The Curl of a Vector Point Function $\underline{F}(x,y,z) = F_1\underline{i} + F_2\underline{j} + F_3\underline{k}$

$$\text{curl}\ \underline{F} = \left(\frac{\partial F_3}{\partial y} - \frac{\partial F_2}{\partial z}\right)\underline{i} + \left(\frac{\partial F_1}{\partial z} - \frac{\partial F_3}{\partial x}\right)\underline{j} + \left(\frac{\partial F_2}{\partial x} - \frac{\partial F_1}{\partial y}\right)\underline{k}$$

$$= \underline{i}\times\frac{\partial \underline{F}}{\partial x} + \underline{j}\times\frac{\partial \underline{F}}{\partial y} + \underline{k}\times\frac{\partial \underline{F}}{\partial z} = \nabla\times\underline{F}$$

$$= \begin{vmatrix} \underline{i} & \underline{j} & \underline{k} \\ \frac{\partial}{\partial x} & \frac{\partial}{\partial y} & \frac{\partial}{\partial z} \\ F_1 & F_2 & F_3 \end{vmatrix}$$

7.14 Compound Operations

7.14.1 div grad $\phi = \nabla.(\nabla\phi) = \nabla^2\phi = \dfrac{\partial^2\phi}{\partial x^2} + \dfrac{\partial^2\phi}{\partial y^2} + \dfrac{\partial^2\phi}{\partial z^2}$.

∇^2 is called the *Laplacian*

7.14.2 div curl $\underline{F} = \nabla.(\nabla\times\underline{F}) = [\nabla\nabla\underline{F}] \equiv 0$

7.14.3 curl grad $\phi = \nabla \times (\nabla\phi) \equiv 0$

7.14.4 curl curl $\underline{F} = \nabla \times (\nabla \times \underline{F}) = \nabla(\nabla.\underline{F}) - \nabla^2 \underline{F}$

where $\nabla^2 \underline{F} \equiv \dfrac{\partial^2 \underline{F}}{\partial x^2} + \dfrac{\partial^2 \underline{F}}{\partial y^2} + \dfrac{\partial^2 \underline{F}}{\partial z^2}$.

7.14.5 The last two results can be used as a definition of the quantity $\nabla^2 \underline{F}$ called the *vector Laplacian* and sometimes written $\square \underline{F}$

i.e. $\nabla^2 \underline{F}$ = grad div $\underline{F}$ - curl curl $\underline{F}$.

Most of the above results can be deduced formally by regarding ∇ as a vector; for example, div curl $\underline{F} = [\nabla\nabla\underline{F}]$ is symbolically a scalar triple product with two terms equal and therefore equal to zero.

7.15 Operations on Sums and Products

7.15.1 $\nabla(\phi + \psi) = \nabla\phi + \nabla\psi$

7.15.2 $\nabla.(\underline{a} + \underline{b}) = \nabla.\underline{a} + \nabla.\underline{b}$

7.15.3 $\nabla \times (\underline{a} + \underline{b}) = \nabla \times \underline{a} + \nabla \times \underline{b}$

7.15.4 $\nabla.(\phi\underline{a}) = (\nabla\phi).\underline{a} + \phi(\nabla.\underline{a})$

7.15.5 $\nabla.(\underline{a} \times \underline{b}) = \underline{b}.(\nabla \times \underline{a}) - \underline{a}.(\nabla \times \underline{b})$

7.15.6 $\nabla \times (\phi\underline{a}) = (\nabla\phi) \times \underline{a} + \phi(\nabla \times \underline{a})$

7.15.7 $\nabla \times (\underline{a} \times \underline{b}) = (\underline{b}.\nabla)\underline{a} - (\underline{a}.\nabla)\underline{b} + \underline{a}(\nabla.\underline{b}) - \underline{b}(\nabla.\underline{a})$

7.15.8 $\nabla(\phi\psi) = \phi\nabla\psi + \psi\nabla\phi$

7.15.9 $\nabla(\underline{a}.\underline{b}) = (\underline{b}.\nabla)\underline{a} + (\underline{a}.\nabla)\underline{b} + \underline{b} \times (\nabla \times \underline{a}) + \underline{a} \times (\nabla \times \underline{b})$

7.16 General Orthogonal Curvilinear Coordinates

7.16.1 $x = x(u_1, u_2, u_3) \qquad y = y(u_1, u_2, u_3) \qquad z = z(u_1, u_2, u_3)$

$$d\underline{r} = dx\,\underline{i} + dy\,\underline{j} + dz\,\underline{k} = h_1 du_1\,\underline{\varepsilon}_1 + h_2 du_2\,\underline{\varepsilon}_2 + h_3 du_3\,\underline{\varepsilon}_3$$

$$h_i^2 = \left(\frac{\partial x}{\partial u_i}\right)^2 + \left(\frac{\partial y}{\partial u_i}\right)^2 + \left(\frac{\partial z}{\partial u_i}\right)^2 \qquad i = 1,2,3$$

7.16.2 Vector Operators

$$\nabla\phi = \frac{1}{h_1}\frac{\partial\phi}{\partial u_1}\underline{\varepsilon}_1 + \frac{1}{h_2}\frac{\partial\phi}{\partial u_2}\underline{\varepsilon}_2 + \frac{1}{h_3}\frac{\partial\phi}{\partial u_3}\underline{\varepsilon}_3$$

$$\nabla.\underline{a} = \frac{1}{h_1 h_2 h_3}\left[\frac{\partial}{\partial u_1}(h_2 h_3 a_1) + \frac{\partial}{\partial u_2}(h_3 h_1 a_2) + \frac{\partial}{\partial u_3}(h_1 h_2 a_3)\right]$$

$$\nabla \times \underline{a} = \frac{1}{h_1 h_2 h_3}\begin{vmatrix} h_1\underline{\varepsilon}_1 & h_2\underline{\varepsilon}_2 & h_3\underline{\varepsilon}_3 \\ \dfrac{\partial}{\partial u_1} & \dfrac{\partial}{\partial u_2} & \dfrac{\partial}{\partial u_3} \\ h_1 a_1 & h_2 a_2 & h_3 a_3 \end{vmatrix}$$

$$\nabla^2\phi = \frac{1}{h_1 h_2 h_3}\left[\frac{\partial}{\partial u_1}\left(\frac{h_2 h_3}{h_1}\frac{\partial\phi}{\partial u_1}\right) + \frac{\partial}{\partial u_2}\left(\frac{h_3 h_1}{h_2}\frac{\partial\phi}{\partial u_2}\right) + \frac{\partial}{\partial u_3}\left(\frac{h_1 h_2}{h_3}\frac{\partial\phi}{\partial u_3}\right)\right]$$

7.17 Cylindrical and Spherical Polar Coordinates

7.17.1 Cylindrical Polar Coordinates (r,θ,z)

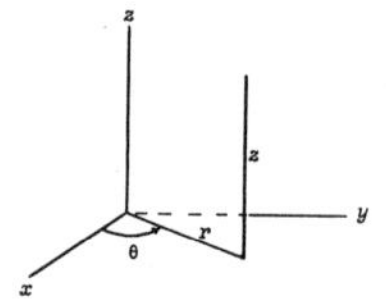

$$\left.\begin{array}{l} x = r\cos\theta,\ y = r\sin\theta,\ z = z \\ \text{where } r \geqslant 0,\ 0 \leqslant \theta < 2\pi,\ -\infty < z < \infty \\ h_1 = 1,\ h_2 = r,\ h_3 = 1 \end{array}\right\}$$

7.17.2 Spherical Polar Coordinates (ρ,ϕ,θ)

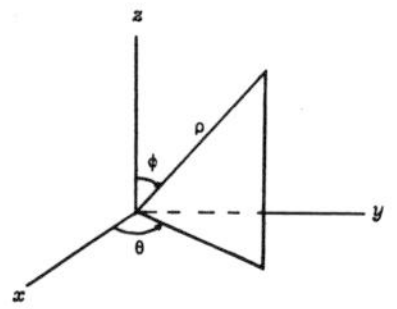

$$\left.\begin{array}{l} x = \rho\sin\phi\cos\theta,\ y = \rho\sin\phi\sin\theta,\ z = \rho\cos\phi \\ \text{where } \rho \geqslant 0,\ 0 \leqslant \phi \leqslant \pi,\ 0 \leqslant \theta < 2\pi. \\ h_1 = 1,\quad h_2 = \rho,\quad h_3 = \rho\sin\phi \end{array}\right\}$$

7.18 Divergence Theorem of Gauss

Let V be a closed bounded region, completely bounded by a piecewise smooth orientable surface S with outward drawn unit normal $\underline{n}$. Then if $\underline{F}(x,y,z)$ is a vector function which is continuous and has continuous first partial derivatives in some domain containing V,

$$\iint_S \underline{n}.\underline{F}\, dS = \iiint_V \text{div } \underline{F}\, dV .$$

7.19 Stokes's Theorem

Let S be a piecewise smooth oriented surface with outward drawn unit normal $\underline{n}$, and having as boundary a piecewise smooth simple closed curve C. Then if $\underline{F}(x,y,z)$ is a vector function which is continuous and has continuous first partial derivatives in any region containing S

$$\oint_C \underline{F}.d\underline{r} = \iint_S \underline{n}.\text{curl } \underline{F}\, dS$$

7.19.1 Green's Theorem in the plane.

If S is a closed region of the xy-plane bounded by a simple closed curve C, and if $P(x,y)$, $Q(x,y)$ are continuous and have continuous first partial derivatives within and on C, then

$$\oint_C (Pdx + Qdy) = \iint_S \left(\frac{\partial Q}{\partial x} - \frac{\partial P}{\partial y}\right) dx\, dy$$

8. MATRICES AND DETERMINANTS

8.1 Matrix definitions

An $m \times n$ *matrix* A is an array of numbers:

$$\begin{array}{rcl}
 & \longleftarrow\; n \text{ columns} \;\longrightarrow & \\
\begin{array}{r} \\ \\ A \;= \\ \\ \text{row } i \longrightarrow \\ \\ \end{array} &
\left[\begin{array}{ccccccc}
a_{11} & a_{12} & a_{13} & \cdot & \cdot & \cdot & a_{1n} \\
a_{21} & a_{22} & a_{23} & \cdot & \cdot & \cdot & a_{2n} \\
\cdot & \cdot & \cdot & \cdot & \cdot & \cdot & \cdot \\
\cdot & \cdot & \cdot & \cdot & \cdot & \cdot & \cdot \\
\cdot & \cdot & \cdot & \cdot & a_{ij} & \cdot & \cdot \\
a_{m1} & a_{m2} & a_{m3} & \cdot & \cdot & \cdot & a_{mn}
\end{array}\right] &
\begin{array}{c} \uparrow \\ \\ m \text{ rows} \\ \\ \downarrow \end{array} \\
 & \begin{array}{ccccccc} \phantom{a_{11}} & \phantom{a_{12}} & \phantom{a_{13}} & & \uparrow & & \phantom{a_{1n}} \\ & & & & \text{column } j & & \end{array} &
\end{array}$$

or $\qquad A = [a_{ij}] \qquad i = 1,2,..,m; \quad j = 1,2,...,n,$

a_{ij} being the *element* in row i, column j. The numbers m and n are the *dimensions* of A, which is *square* if $m = n$. In this case $a_{11}, a_{22}, \ldots, a_{nn}$ form the *principal diagonal* of A, and the *trace* of A is $\operatorname{tr} A = \sum_{i=1}^{n} a_{ii}$.

8.2 Basic matrix operations

8.2.1 Addition

$$[a_{ij}] + [b_{ij}] = [a_{ij} + b_{ij}], \qquad i = 1,2,..,m; \quad j = 1,2,...,n.$$

8.2.2 Multiplication by a scalar

$$k[a_{ij}] = [ka_{ij}]$$

8.2.3 Multiplication of two matrices

The product AB exists only if the number of columns of A is equal to the number of rows of B. If $A = [a_{ij}]$ is $m \times n$ and $B = [b_{ij}]$ is $n \times p$ then $C = AB$ is $m \times p$ and

$$c_{ij} = \sum_{k=1}^{n} a_{ik} b_{kj} = a_{i1} b_{1j} + a_{i2} b_{2j} + \ldots + a_{in} b_{nj},$$

$$i = 1,2,..,m; \; j = 1,2,..p.$$

This is the term-by-term product of the i-th row of A with the j-th column of B.

A and B *commute* with each other if $AB = BA$, but in general $AB \neq BA$.

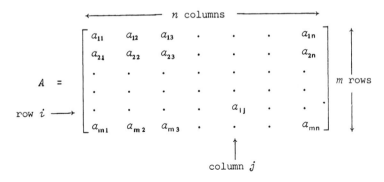

8.3 Diagonal matrix

A square matrix $A = [a_{ij}]$ is *diagonal* if $a_{ij} = 0$ whenever $i \neq j$, written $A = \text{diag}[a_{11}, a_{22}, \ldots, a_{nn}]$
In particular the *unit matrix* $I_n = \text{diag}[1,1,\ldots,1]$ has the property $AI_n = I_n A = A$ for any $n \times n$ matrix A.

8.4 Transpose

8.4.1 Definitions

If $A = [a_{ij}]$ is $m \times n$ then the *transpose* of A is

$$A^T = [a_{ji}] \qquad j = 1,2,..,n; \quad i = 1,2,..,m.$$

When A has complex elements, its *conjugate* is

$$\bar{A} = [\bar{a}_{ij}]$$

and the *conjugate transpose*

$$A^* = (\bar{A})^T = [\bar{a}_{ji}] .$$

8.4.2 Properties

$$(A^T)^T = A; \qquad (AB)^T = B^T A^T; \qquad (A^*)^* = A; \qquad (AB)^* = B^* A^*.$$

8.5 Determinant

A scalar function of an $n \times n$ matrix A is its *determinant* det A or $|A|$.
When $n = 2$,

$$\det A = \begin{vmatrix} a_{11} & a_{12} \\ a_{21} & a_{22} \end{vmatrix} = a_{11} a_{22} - a_{12} a_{21} .$$

The determinant of an $n \times n$ matrix can be evaluated by expressing it in terms of determinants of order n-1, as follows:

$$\det A = \sum_{k=1}^{n} a_{ik} A_{ik} \qquad \text{(expansion by the } i\text{-th row)}$$

or $$\det A = \sum_{k=1}^{n} a_{kj} A_{kj} \qquad \text{(expansion by the } j\text{-th column)}$$

for each $i,j = 1,2,\ldots,n$,

where A_{ij} is the *cofactor* of the element a_{ij}, being $(-1)^{i+j}$ times the determinant of order n-1 obtained by deleting row i and column j in det A (this latter determinant is the *minor* of a_{ij}). For example, expanding by the second column,

$$\begin{vmatrix} a_{11} & a_{12} & a_{13} \\ a_{21} & a_{22} & a_{23} \\ a_{31} & a_{32} & a_{33} \end{vmatrix} = -a_{12} \begin{vmatrix} a_{21} & a_{23} \\ a_{31} & a_{33} \end{vmatrix} + a_{22} \begin{vmatrix} a_{11} & a_{13} \\ a_{31} & a_{33} \end{vmatrix} - a_{32} \begin{vmatrix} a_{11} & a_{13} \\ a_{21} & a_{23} \end{vmatrix} .$$

N.B. $$\sum_{k=1}^{n} a_{ik} A_{jk} = 0 = \sum_{k=1}^{n} a_{ki} A_{kj} \qquad \text{if } i \neq j .$$

8.6 Inverse

8.6.1 Definition

If A is $n \times n$ and $\det A \neq 0$ then A is *nonsingular* and a matrix A^{-1}, the *inverse* of A, exists such that

$$AA^{-1} = A^{-1}A = I_n .$$

If $\det A = 0$, A is *singular*.

8.6.2 Explicit form

$$A^{-1} = \text{Adj } A/\det A,$$

where Adj A, the *adjoint* of A, is the transpose of the matrix of cofactors, i.e. $\text{Adj } A = [A_{ji}]$.

8.6.3 Properties

$$(AB)^{-1} = B^{-1}A^{-1}; \quad (A^{T})^{-1} = (A^{-1})^{T}; \quad (A^*)^{-1} = (A^{-1})^*.$$

8.7 Rank

8.7.1 Definition

If A is an $m \times n$ matrix then any k rows ($k \leqslant m$) and ℓ columns ($\ell \leqslant n$) of A form a $k \times \ell$ *submatrix* of A. The *rank* of A, $R(A)$, is the order of the largest nonsingular square submatrix of A. In particular, when $m = n$ then $R(A) = n$ if and only if A is nonsingular.

The maximum number of linearly independent rows of A, and the maximum number of linearly independent columns of A, is each equal to $R(A)$.

8.7.2 Properties

$R(A) = 0$ if and only if $A = 0$; $R(A^{T}) = R(A)$; $R(A+B) \leqslant R(A) + R(B)$.

$R(A) + R(B) - n \leqslant R(AB) \leqslant \min\{R(A), R(B)\}$, where B is $n \times p$.

If $B = PAQ$, with P and Q nonsingular, then $R(B) = R(A)$, and B is *equivalent* to A.

8.8 Linear equations

A system of m equations in n unknowns

$$\sum_{j=1}^{n} a_{ij}x_j = b_i, \quad i = 1,2,\ldots,m$$

can be written $Ax = b$ where $A = [a_{ij}]$, $x = [x_1,x_2,\ldots,x_n]^{T}$, $b = [b_1,b_2,\ldots,b_m]^{T}$. Define the $m \times (n+1)$ matrix $B = [A,b]$. Then $R(A) \leqslant R(B)$ and the equations possess

(i) a unique solution if and only if $R(A) = R(B) = n$

(ii) an infinite number of solutions if and only if $R(A) = R(B) < n$

(iii) no solution if and only if $R(A) < R(B)$.

In case (i) when A is square the solution is $x = A^{-1}b$.

8.9 Kronecker product

8.9.1 Definition

If $A = [a_{ij}]$ is $m \times n$ and B is $p \times q$ then $A \otimes B$ is the $mp \times nq$ matrix which, if regarded as partitioned, has i, j block $a_{ij}B$, $i = 1,\ldots,m$; $j = 1,\ldots,n$.

8.9.2 Properties

$$(A \otimes B)^T = A^T \otimes B^T; \qquad (A \otimes B)^* = A^* \otimes B^*.$$

If $m = n$, $p = q$ then

$$\det(A \otimes B) = (\det A)^q (\det B)^n; \qquad (A \otimes B)^{-1} = A^{-1} \otimes B^{-1}.$$

If C is $n \times r$ and D is $q \times s$ then

$$(A \otimes B)(C \otimes D) = AC \otimes BD.$$

If $v(A) = [a_{11}, a_{12}, \ldots, a_{1n}, a_{21}, \ldots, a_{2n}, \ldots, a_{m1}, \ldots, a_{mn}]^T$, then

$$v(AXB) = (A \otimes B^T)v(X).$$

A *permutation* matrix P has a single unit element in each row and column, all other elements being zero, and $P^TP = I$. There exist permutation matrices P_1, P_2 such that

$$A \otimes B = P_1(B \otimes A)P_2$$

and P_1, P_2 depend only upon m, p and n, q respectively.

8.10 Eigenvalues and eigenvectors

8.10.1 Characteristic polynomial of an n × n matrix

$$\det(\lambda I_n - A) = \lambda^n + a_1\lambda^{n-1} + a_2\lambda^{n-2} + \ldots + a_{n-1}\lambda + a_n = a(\lambda)$$

8.10.2 Eigenvalues (or characteristic roots)

The n roots $\lambda_1, \ldots, \lambda_n$ of $a(\lambda) = 0$.

$$\sum_{i=1}^{n} \lambda_i = \operatorname{tr} A; \qquad \lambda_1\lambda_2\ldots\lambda_n = \det A.$$

8.10.3 Eigenvectors (or characteristic vectors)

A column vector $w_i = [w_{i1}, \ldots, w_{in}]^T$ is a *right* eigenvector of A if

$$Aw_i = \lambda_i w_i, \quad \text{or equivalently } (\lambda I - A)w_i = 0$$

A row vector v_i is a *left* eigenvector of A if

$$v_iA = \lambda_i v_i, \quad \text{or equivalently } v_i(\lambda I - A) = 0$$

A *normalised* eigenvector satisfies

$$|w_i| = (w_{i1}^2 + w_{i2}^2 + \ldots + w_{in}^2)^{1/2} = 1.$$

8.10.4 Special matrices

matrix A	definition	eigenvalues
real symmetric	$A^T = A$	all real
Hermitian	$A^* = A$	all real
real skew-symmetric	$A^T = -A$	all imaginary (including zero)
skew-Hermitian	$A^* = -A$	all imaginary (including zero)
real orthogonal	$A^TA = AA^T = I$	all $\lvert\lambda_i\rvert = 1$
unitary	$A^*A = AA^* = I$	all $\lvert\lambda_i\rvert = 1$
normal	$A^*A = AA^*$	

8.10.5 Related matrices

matrix	eigenvalues
A $(n \times n)$	λ_i, $i = 1, 2, \ldots, n$
A^T	λ_i
A^{-1}	λ_i^{-1}, provided all $\lambda_i \neq 0$
A^p	λ_i^p, p = integer (holds if $p < 0$, provided all $\lambda_i \neq 0$)
A^*	$\bar{\lambda}_i$
B $(m \times m)$	μ_j, $j = 1, 2, \ldots, m$
$A \otimes B$	$\lambda_i \mu_j$
$A \otimes I_m + I_n \otimes B$	$\lambda_i + \mu_j$

8.10.6 Cayley-Hamilton theorem

Every square matrix satisfies its own characteristic polynomial,

i.e. $$A^n + a_1 A^{n-1} + a_2 A^{n-2} + \ldots + a_{n-1} A + a_n I = 0.$$

8.10.7 Diagonalisation

If the λ_i are all different from each other, the vectors $w_1, w_2, \ldots, w_n$ are linearly independent, and

$$W^{-1}AW = \text{diag}[\lambda_1, \lambda_2, \ldots, \lambda_n]$$

where $W = [w_1, w_2, \ldots, w_n]$.

8.10.8 Similarity

If $B = PAP^{-1}$ with P nonsingular, then A and B are *similar*, and have the same eigenvalues.

8.10.9 Jordan canonical form

Any square matrix A is similar to the *Jordan form*

$$\text{diag}[J_1, J_2, \ldots, J_k]$$

where J_i is an $n_i \times n_i$ *Jordan block*

$$J_i = \begin{bmatrix} \lambda & 1 & 0 & . & . & 0 \\ 0 & \lambda & 1 & . & . & 0 \\ . & . & . & . & . & 0 \\ . & . & . & . & \lambda & 1 \\ . & . & . & . & 0 & \lambda \end{bmatrix}$$

corresponding to an eigenvalue λ, and $\sum_{i=1}^{k} n_i = n$.

If λ_r occurs only once it appears only in the 1×1 block $[\lambda_r]$. There may be more than one block corresponding to λ_s if it occurs p_s (> 1) times, and the sum of the orders of these blocks equals p_s. The numbers k, $n_1, n_2, \ldots, n_k$ are uniquely determined by A.

8.11 Quadratic and Hermitian forms

8.11.1 Quadratic form

$$q(x) = \sum_{i=1}^{n} \sum_{j=1}^{n} a_{ij} x_i x_j = x^T A x$$

where $x^T = [x_1, x_2, \ldots, x_n]$, $A = [a_{ij}]$ is real, symmetric.

8.11.2 Hermitian form

$$h(x) = \sum_{i=1}^{n} \sum_{j=1}^{n} a_{ij} \bar{x}_i x_j = x^* A x, \quad \text{with } A \text{ Hermitian.}$$

8.11.3 Sign properties

A form $f(x)$ [$= q(x)$ in 8.11.1 or $h(x)$ in 8.11.2] is

positive (negative) definite: if $f(x) > 0$ (< 0) for $x \neq 0$;
if and only if all $\lambda_i > 0$ (< 0).

positive (negative) semidefinite: if $f(x) \geqslant 0$ ($\leqslant 0$) for all x;
if and only if all $\lambda_i \geqslant 0$ ($\leqslant 0$).

indefinite: if $f(x) > 0$ and $f(x) < 0$ for some values of x;
if and only if $\lambda_i > 0$, $\lambda_j < 0$ for some i, j.

where λ_i are the eigenvalues of A.

8.11.4 Relationships

For A real, symmetric, P nonsingular: $B = P^T A P$ is *congruent* to A.

For A Hermitian, P nonsingular: $B = P^* A P$ is *conjunctive* to A.

8.11.5 Sylvester's law of inertia

It is always possible to reduce a quadratic form $q(x)$ to a sum of squares by a nonsingular transformation $y = Px$, i.e.

$$q(y) = y^T P^T A P y = \sum_{i=1}^{r} \alpha_i y_i^2$$

where $y^T = [y_1, \ldots, y_n]$ and $r = R(A)$. Irrespective of the choice of P:

the number of positive α's = number of positive eigenvalues of $A = \pi$

the number of negative α's = number of negative eigenvalues of $A = \nu$.

The same result holds for Hermitian forms, the sum of squares being $\sum_{i=1}^{r} \alpha_i |y_i|^2$.

The *signature* of the form (or the associated matrix) is $\pi - \nu$.

9. NUMERICAL METHODS

9.1 Tabulated Values and Difference Tables

9.1.1 $f(x) \equiv f(x_0 + ph) \equiv f(x_p) \equiv f_p$

The variable p is continuous but the function is generally defined by tabulation for integral values of p.

9.1.2

Function	Differences 1st	2nd	3rd	4th
f_0				
	$f_1 - f_0$			
f_1		$f_2 - 2f_1 + f_0$		
	$f_2 - f_1$		$f_3 - 3f_2 + 3f_1 - f_0$	
f_2		$f_3 - 2f_2 + f_1$		$f_4 - 4f_3 + 6f_2 - 4f_1 + f_0$
	$f_3 - f_2$		$f_4 - 3f_3 + 3f_2 - f_1$	
f_3		$f_4 - 2f_3 + f_2$		
	$f_4 - f_3$			
f_4				

In the table any difference is the result of subtracting the value diagonally above it to the left from the value diagonally below it to the left.

9.2 Notation for differences

There are three common notations in use for the differences in 9.1.2, illustrated by writing the first difference $f_{p+1} - f_p$ in terms of each:

9.2.1 $\Delta_p = \Delta f_p = f_{p+1} - f_p$ Forward difference

9.2.2 $\delta_{p+\frac{1}{2}} = \delta f_{p+\frac{1}{2}} = f_{p+1} - f_p$ Central difference

9.2.3 $\nabla_{p+1} = \nabla f_{p+1} = f_{p+1} - f_p$ Backward difference

9.2.4 Table 9.1.2 in terms of the three notations

Forward differences

	1st	2nd	3rd	4th
f_0				
	Δ_0			
f_1		Δ_0^2		
	Δ_1		Δ_0^3	
f_2		Δ_1^2		Δ_0^4
	Δ_2		Δ_1^3	
f_3		Δ_2^2		
	Δ_3			
f_4				

Central differences

	1st	2nd	3rd	4th
f_0				
	$\delta_{\frac{1}{2}}$			
f_1		δ_1^2		
	$\delta_{1\frac{1}{2}}$		$\delta_{1\frac{1}{2}}^3$	
f_2		δ_2^2		δ_2^4
	$\delta_{2\frac{1}{2}}$		$\delta_{2\frac{1}{2}}^3$	
f_3		δ_3^2		
	$\delta_{3\frac{1}{2}}$			
f_4				

Backward differences

	1st	2nd	3rd	4th
f_0				
	∇_1			
f_1		∇_2^2		
	∇_2		∇_3^3	
f_2		∇_3^2		∇_4^4
	∇_3		∇_4^3	
f_3		∇_4^2		
	∇_4			
f_4				

The higher differences are obtained by repeating the operations e.g. a second difference = the 1st difference of a first difference.

9.2.5 $\Delta^n_{p-\frac{1}{2}n} = \delta^n_p = \nabla^n_{p+\frac{1}{2}n}$.

In all these cases the notation is condensed as much as is possible without causing ambiguity, thus for example

$$\Delta^2_p \equiv \Delta^2 f_p \equiv \Delta^2 f(x_p) \quad .$$

9.3 Finite Difference Operators

9.3.1 Definitions of the operators

Symbol	Operator	Definition
E	Displacement	$Ef_p = f_{p+1}$
Δ	Forward Difference	$\Delta f_p = f_{p+1} - f_p$
δ	Central Difference	$\delta f_p = f_{p+\frac{1}{2}} - f_{p-\frac{1}{2}}$
∇	Backward Difference	$\nabla f_p = f_p - f_{p-1}$
μ	Averaging	$\mu f_p = (f_{p+\frac{1}{2}} + f_{p-\frac{1}{2}})/2$
D	Differentiation	$Df_p = \dfrac{df(x)}{dx} = \dfrac{1}{h}\dfrac{df_p}{dp}$
$I = D^{-1}$	Integration	$If_p = \int_0^x f(x)dx = h\int_0^p f_p dp$

9.3.2 Relationships between Operators

	E	Δ	δ,μ	∇	D
E	E	$1+\Delta$	$1+\mu\delta+\frac{1}{2}\delta^2$	$(1-\nabla)^{-1}$	e^{hD}
Δ	$E-1$	Δ	$\mu\delta+\frac{1}{2}\delta^2$	$\nabla(1-\nabla)^{-1}$	$e^{hD}-1$
δ	$E^{\frac{1}{2}} - E^{-\frac{1}{2}}$	$\Delta(1+\Delta)^{-\frac{1}{2}}$	δ	$\nabla(1-\nabla)^{-\frac{1}{2}}$	$2\sinh(\frac{1}{2}hD)$
∇	$1-E^{-1}$	$\Delta(1+\Delta)^{-1}$	$\mu\delta - \frac{1}{2}\delta^2$	∇	$1-e^{-hD}$
μ	$(E^{\frac{1}{2}}+E^{-\frac{1}{2}})/2$	$\frac{1}{2}(2+\Delta)(1+\Delta)^{-\frac{1}{2}}$	$(1+\frac{1}{4}\delta^2)^{\frac{1}{2}}$	$\frac{1}{2}(2-\nabla)(1-\nabla)^{-\frac{1}{2}}$	$\cosh(\frac{1}{2}hD)$
hD	$\ln E$	$\ln(1+\Delta)$	$2\sinh^{-1}\frac{1}{2}\delta$	$-\ln(1-\nabla)$	hD

9.3.3 Composition of operators

This is done using the definitions in 9.3.1.

For example, $\mu\delta_p = \mu(\delta f_p) = \frac{1}{2}\left(\delta f_{p+\frac{1}{2}} + \delta f_{p-\frac{1}{2}}\right) = \frac{1}{2}\left(\delta_{p+\frac{1}{2}} + \delta_{p-\frac{1}{2}}\right)$

$$\left[= \tfrac{1}{2}(f_{p+1} - f_{p-1})\right]$$

9.4 Two useful formulae

9.4.1 Symbolic form of Taylor's series

$$f_p = E^p f_0 = (e^{hD})^p f_0 = f_0 + phDf_0 + \frac{p^2 h^2 D^2 f_0}{2!} + \dots$$

9.4.2 A summation formula

$$f_0 + f_1 + \dots + f_{n-1} = \sum_{r=1}^{n} \binom{n}{r} \Delta_0^{\,r-1}$$

Note: this can be applied to obtain $\sum_{r=1}^{n} r^k$.

9.5 Interpolation formulae

9.5.1 Newton's Forward Difference formula

$$f_p = f_0 + p\Delta_0 + \frac{p(p-1)}{2!}\Delta_0^2 + \frac{p(p-1)(p-2)}{3!}\Delta_0^3 + \dots$$

9.5.2 Newton's Backward Difference formula

$$f_p = f_0 + p\nabla_0 + \frac{p(p+1)}{2!}\nabla_0^2 + \frac{p(p+1)(p+2)}{3!}\nabla_0^3 + \dots$$

9.5.3 Bessel's formula

$$f_p = f_0 + p\delta_{1/2} + \frac{p(p-1)}{4}(\delta_0^2 + \delta_1^2) + \frac{p(p-1)(2p-1)}{12}\delta_{1/2}^3$$

$$+ \frac{(p+1)p(p-1)(p-2)}{48}(\delta_0^4 + \delta_1^4) + \dots, 0 \leqslant p \leqslant 1$$

9.5.4 Everett's formula

$$f_p = (1-p)f_0 + pf_1 - \frac{p(p-1)(p-2)}{3!}\delta_0^2 + \frac{(p+1)p(p-1)}{3!}\delta_1^2$$

$$- \frac{(p+1)p(p-1)(p-2)(p-3)}{5!}\delta_0^4$$

$$+ \frac{(p+2)(p+1)p(p-1)(p-2)}{5!}\delta_1^4 + \dots \qquad 0 \leqslant p \leqslant 1$$

9.5.5 Stirling's formula

$$f_p = f_0 + \tfrac{1}{2}p(\delta_{1/2} + \delta_{-1/2}) + \tfrac{1}{2}p^2\delta_0^2 + \tfrac{1}{2}\binom{p+1}{3}(\delta_{1/2}^3 + \delta_{-1/2}^3)$$

$$+ \frac{p}{4}\binom{p+1}{3}\delta_0^4 + \dots \qquad -\tfrac{1}{2} \leqslant p \leqslant \tfrac{1}{2}$$

9.5.6 Lagrange's formula

The nth degree polynomial through the $n+1$ points (x_r, f_r), $r = 0,1,2\dots n$, is

$$P_n(x) = \sum_{r=0}^{n} f(x_r) \prod_{\substack{i=0 \\ i \neq r}}^{n} \left(\frac{x - x_i}{x_r - x_i}\right)$$

where $f_r = f(x_r)$.

9.6 Derivatives

Prime is used to denote differentiation with respect to x, thus

$$f'_p = \frac{d}{dx} f(x_0 + ph) = \frac{1}{h}\frac{d}{dp} f_p$$

Derivatives at a tabular point

9.6.1 $$hf'_0 = \mu\delta_0 - \frac{1}{6}\mu\delta_0^3 + \frac{1}{30}\mu\delta_0^5 - \dots$$

9.6.2 $$h^2 f''_0 = \delta_0^2 - \frac{1}{12}\delta_0^4 + \frac{1}{90}\delta_0^6 - \dots$$

9.6.3 $$h^n f_0^{(n)} \simeq \delta_0^n \ (n \text{ even}); \quad \simeq \mu\delta_0^n \ (n \text{ odd}).$$

Derivatives at a half-way point

9.6.4 $$hf'_{1/2} = \delta_{1/2} - \frac{1}{24}\delta_{1/2}^3 + \frac{3}{640}\delta_{1/2}^5 - \dots$$

9.6.5 $$h^2 f''_{1/2} = \mu\delta_{1/2}^2 - \frac{5}{24}\mu\delta_{1/2}^4 + \frac{259}{5760}\mu\delta_{1/2}^6 - \dots$$

9.7 Integration

9.7.1 Trapezoidal Rule

$$\int_{x_0}^{x_n} f(x)dx \simeq \frac{h}{2}\left[f_0 + 2f_1 + 2f_2 + \dots + 2f_{n-1} + f_n\right] - \frac{nh^3}{12} f^{(2)}(\xi)$$

9.7.2 Simpson's Rule

$$\int_{x_0}^{x_{2n}} f(x)dx \simeq \frac{h}{3}\left[f_0 + 4f_1 + 2f_2 + 4f_3 + \dots + 2f_{2n-2} + 4f_{2n-1} + f_{2n}\right] - \frac{nh^5}{90} f^{(4)}(\xi)$$

The number of intervals must be even.

9.7.3 $$\int_{x_0}^{x_n} f(x)dx = h\left[\tfrac{1}{2}f_0 + f_1 + f_2 + \dots + f_{n-1} + \tfrac{1}{2}f_n - \left(\frac{1}{12}\mu\delta - \frac{11}{720}\mu\delta^3 + \dots\right)\left(f_n - f_0\right)\right]$$

9.7.4 $$\int_{x_{1/2}}^{x_{n+1/2}} f(x)dx = h\left[f_1 + f_2 + \dots + f_n + \left(\frac{1}{24}\delta - \frac{17}{5760}\delta^3 + \dots\right)\left(f_{n+1/2} - f_{1/2}\right)\right]$$

9.7.5 $$\int_{x_0}^{x_{n+1/2}} f(x)dx = h\left[\tfrac{1}{2}f_0 + f_1 + f_2 + \dots + f_{n-1} + f_n + \left(\frac{1}{24}\delta - \frac{17}{5760}\delta^3\right)f_{n+1/2} + \left(\frac{1}{12}\mu\delta - \frac{11}{720}\mu\delta^3 + \dots\right)f_0\right]$$

9.7.6 $$\int_{x_0}^{x_n} f(x)dx = h\left[\tfrac{1}{2}f_0 + f_1 + \dots + f_{n-1} + \tfrac{1}{2}f_n - \frac{1}{12}\left(\nabla_n - \Delta_0\right) - \frac{1}{24}\left(\nabla_n^2 + \Delta_0^2\right) - \frac{19}{720}\left(\nabla_n^3 - \Delta_0^3\right) - \frac{3}{160}\left(\nabla_n^4 + \Delta_0^4\right) + \dots\right]$$

9.8 Iterative processes

9.8.1 Newton-Raphson Method for finding the roots of an equation

$$x_{n+1} = x_n - \frac{f(x_n)}{f'(x_n)}, \quad n = 1, 2, 3, \ldots$$

provides successively closer approximations to a root of $f(x) = 0$, where x_0 is an initial approximation.

9.8.2 Aitken's δ^2-process for convergence acceleration

If $\lim_{n\to\infty} x_n = x$ and the errors $\{x - x_n\}$ are approximately in geometric progression then $x^*_{n+2} = x_{n+2} - \dfrac{(x_{n+2} - x_{n+1})^2}{x_{n+2} - 2x_{n+1} + x_n}$ is an improved estimate of x_{n+2}.

9.9 Ordinary differential equations $y' = f(x, y)$

9.9.1 Runge-Kutta (second order)

$$y_{n+1} = y_n + \tfrac{1}{2}(k_1 + k_2); \quad k_1 = hf(x_n, y_n), \quad k_2 = hf(x_n + h, y_n + k_1)$$

9.9.2 Runge-Kutta (fourth order)

$$y_{n+1} = y_n + \frac{1}{6}\left[k_1 + 2k_2 + 2k_3 + k_4\right]$$

$$k_1 = hf(x_n, y_n) \qquad k_2 = hf(x_n + \tfrac{1}{2}h, y_n + \tfrac{1}{2}k_1)$$

$$k_3 = hf(x_n + \tfrac{1}{2}h, y_n + \tfrac{1}{2}k_2) \qquad k_4 = hf(x_n + h, y_n + k_3)$$

9.9.3 Predictor-corrector $\left[f_n = f(x_n, y_n)\right]$

	2nd Order	Milne
Predictor y^P_{n+1}	$y_{n-1} + 2hf_n$	$y_{n-3} + \frac{4}{3}h(2f_{n-2} - f_{n-1} + 2f_n)$
Corrector y^C_{n+1}	$y_n + \frac{1}{2}h(f_n + f_{n+1})$	$y_{n-1} + \frac{1}{3}h(f_{n-1} + 4f_n + f_{n+1})$
Error estimate $y_{n+1} - y^C_{n+1}$	$\frac{1}{5}(y^P_{n+1} - y^C_{n+1})$	$\frac{1}{29}(y^P_{n+1} - y^C_{n+1})$

9.9.4 Adams-Bashforth-Moulton

$$\text{Predictor } y^P_{n+1} = y_n + \frac{1}{24}h(55f_n - 59f_{n-1} + 37f_{n-2} - 9f_{n-3})$$

$$\text{Corrector } y^C_{n+1} = y_n + \frac{1}{24}h(9f_{n+1} + 19f_n - 5f_{n-1} + f_{n-2})$$

$$y_{n+1} - y^C_{n+1} \approx \frac{19}{270}(y^P_{n+1} - y^C_{n+1})$$

9.10 Systems of differential equations (simultaneous first order)

$$y' = f(x, y, z) \qquad z' = g(x, y, z)$$

9.10.1 Runge-Kutta (second order)

$$y_{n+1} = y_n + \tfrac{1}{2}(k_1 + k_2);\ k_1 = hf(x_n, y_n, z_n),\ k_2 = hf(x_n + h,\ y_n + k_1,\ z_n + l_1)$$
$$z_{n+1} = z_n + \tfrac{1}{2}(l_1 + l_2);\ l_1 = hg(x_n, y_n, z_n),\ l_2 = hg(x_n + h,\ y_n + k_1,\ z_n + l_1)$$

9.10.2 Runge-Kutta (fourth order)

$$y_{n+1} = y_n + \frac{1}{6}\left[k_1 + 2k_2 + 2k_3 + k_4\right], \qquad z_{n+1} = z_n + \frac{1}{6}\left[l_1 + 2l_2 + 2l_3 + l_4\right]$$

$$k_1 = hf(x_n, y_n, z_n) \qquad l_1 = hg(x_n, y_n, z_n)$$
$$k_2 = hf(x_n + \tfrac{1}{2}h,\ y_n + \tfrac{1}{2}k_1,\ z_n + \tfrac{1}{2}l_1) \qquad l_2 = hg(x_n + \tfrac{1}{2}h,\ y_n + \tfrac{1}{2}k_1,\ z_n + \tfrac{1}{2}l_1)$$
$$k_3 = hf(x_n + \tfrac{1}{2}h,\ y_n + \tfrac{1}{2}k_2,\ z_n + \tfrac{1}{2}l_2) \qquad l_3 = hg(x_n + \tfrac{1}{2}h,\ y_n + \tfrac{1}{2}k_2,\ z_n + \tfrac{1}{2}l_2)$$
$$k_4 = hf(x_n + h,\ y_n + k_3,\ z_n + l_3) \qquad l_4 = hg(x_n + h,\ y_n + k_3,\ z_n + l_3)$$

9.11 Higher order equations

These can be changed to a system of first order equations. e.g. if $y'' = F(x, y, z')$ set $y' = z$ and replace the equation by

$z' = F(x, y, z)$ and $y' = z$, when 9.10 can be used.

9.12 Chebyshev polynomials

9.12.1 $T_n(x) = \cos(n\cos^{-1}x)$, $-1 \leqslant x \leqslant 1$, $\quad T_{n+1}(x) = 2xT_n(x) - T_{n-1}(x)$,

$T_0 = 1$, $T_1 = x$, $T_2 = 2x^2 - 1$, $T_3 = 4x^3 - 3x$, $T_4 = 8x^4 - 8x^2 + 1$

9.12.2 $$\int_{-1}^{1} \frac{T_m(x)T_n(x)}{\sqrt{(1-x^2)}}\,dx = \begin{cases} 0, & m \neq n \\ \pi/2, & m = n \neq 0 \\ \pi, & m = n = 0 \end{cases}$$

9.12.3 $$\sum_{i=0}^{n}{}'' T_r(x_i)T_s(x_i) = \begin{cases} n, & r = s = 0 \text{ or } n \\ n/2, & r = s \neq 0 \text{ or } n \\ 0, & r \neq s \end{cases} \quad \begin{matrix} r,s \leqslant n > 0 \\ x_i = \cos\left(\frac{\pi i}{n}\right) \end{matrix}$$

$$\left(\text{notation: } \sum_{i=0}^{n}{}'' u_i = \tfrac{1}{2}u_0 + u_1 + u_2 + \ldots + u_{n-1} + \tfrac{1}{2}u_n\right)$$

9.12.4 $$x^r T_s(x) = 2^{-r} \sum_{i=0}^{r} \binom{r}{i} T_{|s-r+2i|}(x)$$

9.12.5 $$T_r(x)T_s(x) = \tfrac{1}{2}\left[T_{r+s}(x) + T_{|r-s|}(x)\right]$$

9.12.6 The Chebyshev series of a function $f(x)$ in the range $-1 \leqslant x \leqslant 1$ is given by

$$f(x) = \sum_{r=0}^{\infty}{}' a_r T_r(x) \qquad \left(\text{notation: } \sum_{r=0}^{n}{}' u_r = \tfrac{1}{2}u_0 + u_1 + u_2 + \ldots + u_n\right)$$

where $$a_r = \frac{2}{\pi}\int_0^{\pi} f(\cos\theta)\cos r\theta\,d\theta = \frac{2}{\pi}\int_{-1}^{1} \frac{f(x)T_r(x)}{\sqrt{(1-x^2)}}\,dx .$$

$$\int f(x)dx = \text{const.} + \sum_{r=1}^{\infty} \frac{1}{2r}\left(a_{r-1} - a_{r+1}\right) T_r(x)$$

For the general interval $a \leqslant x \leqslant b$, set $u = (a + b - 2x)/(a - b)$, then $-1 \leqslant u \leqslant 1$.

9.13 Orthogonal polynomials $p_n(x)$

9.13.1 Orthogonality relations

$$\int_a^b w(x)p_m(x)\,p_n(x)dx = h_n\delta_{mn}$$

Name of polynomial	Symbol	$w(x)$	a	b	h_n
Chebyshev of first kind	$T_n(x)$	$(1-x^2)^{-\frac{1}{2}}$	-1	1	$\pi/2\ (n \neq 0);\ \pi\ (n=0)$
Chebyshev of second kind	$U_n(x)$	$(1-x^2)^{\frac{1}{2}}$	-1	1	$\pi/2$
Shifted $T_n(x)$	$T_n^*(x)$	$(x-x^2)^{-\frac{1}{2}}$	0	1	$\pi/2\ (n \neq 0);\ \pi\ (n=0)$
Shifted $U_n(x)$	$U_n^*(x)$	$(x-x^2)^{\frac{1}{2}}$	0	1	$\pi/8$
Legendre	$P_n(x)$	1	-1	1	$2/(2n+1)$
Hermite	$H_n(x)$	$\exp(-x^2)$	$-\infty$	∞	$\pi^{\frac{1}{2}}2^n n!$
Laguerre	$L_n(x)$	e^{-x}	0	∞	1
Generalised Laguerre	$L_n^\alpha(x)$	$e^{-x}x^\alpha$	0	∞	$\Gamma(n+\alpha+1)/n!$
Ultraspherical (Gegenbauer)	$C_n^\alpha(x)$ $\alpha \neq 0$	$(1-x^2)^{\alpha-\frac{1}{2}}$ $\alpha > -\frac{1}{2}$	-1	1	$\dfrac{\pi 2^{1-2\alpha}\Gamma(n+2\alpha)}{n!(n+\alpha)[\Gamma(\alpha)]^2}$

9.13.2 Recurrence relations

$$p_n(x) = (\alpha_n x + \beta_n)p_{n-1}(x) - \gamma_n p_{n-2}(x), \quad n = 2, 3, 4, \ldots; \quad p_0(x) = 1$$

$p_n(x)$	α_n	β_n	γ_n	$p_1(x)$
$T_n(x)$	2	0	1	x
$U_n(x)$	2	0	1	$2x$
$T_n^*(x)$	4	-2	1	$2x-1$
$U_n^*(x)$	4	-2	1	$4x-2$
$P_n(x)$	$\dfrac{2n-1}{n}$	0	$\dfrac{n-1}{n}$	x
$H_n(x)$	2	0	$2n-2$	$2x$
$L_n(x)$	$-\dfrac{1}{n}$	$\dfrac{2n-1}{n}$	$\dfrac{n-1}{n}$	$1-x$
$L_n^\alpha(x)$ $\alpha > -1$	$-\dfrac{1}{n}$	$\dfrac{\alpha+2n-1}{n}$	$\dfrac{\alpha+n-1}{n}$	$\alpha+1-x$
$C_n^\alpha(x)$ $\alpha > -\frac{1}{2}$	$\dfrac{2\alpha+2n-2}{n}$	0	$\dfrac{2\alpha+n-2}{n}$	$2\alpha x\ (\alpha \neq 0)$ $2x\ (\alpha = 0)$

9.13.3 Generating functions and Rodrigues' forms

$p_n(x)$	$G(x,t) = \sum_{n=0}^{\infty} g_n p_n(x) t^n$: $G(x,t)$	g_n	Rodrigues-type form for $p_n(x)$
$T_n(x)$	$\dfrac{1 - xt}{1 - 2xt + t^2}$	1	$\dfrac{(-2)^n n!(1 - x^2)^{1/2}}{(2n)!} \dfrac{d^n}{dx^n} (1 - x^2)^{n-1/2}$
$U_n(x)$	$\dfrac{1}{1 - 2xt + t^2}$	1	$\dfrac{(-2)^n (n+1)!}{(2n+1)!(1 - x^2)^{1/2}} \dfrac{d^n}{dx^n} (1 - x^2)^{n+1/2}$
$P_n(x)$	$\dfrac{1}{(1 - 2xt + t^2)^{1/2}}$	1	$\dfrac{1}{2^n n!} \dfrac{d^n}{dx^n} (x^2 - 1)^n$
$H_n(x)$	$\exp(2xt - t^2)$	$\dfrac{1}{n!}$	$(-1)^n e^{x^2} \dfrac{d^n}{dx^n} \left(e^{-x^2}\right)$
$L_n(x)$	$\dfrac{\exp[xt/(t-1)]}{1 - t}$	1	$\dfrac{e^x}{n!} \dfrac{d^n}{dx^n} \left(e^{-x} x^n\right)$
$L_n^{\alpha}(x)$, $\alpha > -1$	$\dfrac{\exp[xt/(t-1)]}{(1 - t)^{\alpha+1}}$	1	$\dfrac{e^x x^{-\alpha}}{n!} \dfrac{d^n}{dx^n} \left(e^{-x} x^{\alpha+n}\right)$
$C_n^{\alpha}(x)$, $\alpha \neq 0$, $\alpha > -\frac{1}{2}$	$\dfrac{1}{(1 - 2xt + t^2)^{\alpha}}$	1	$k_n (1 - x^2)^{1/2-\alpha} \dfrac{d^n}{dx^n} (1 - x^2)^{\alpha+n-1/2}$, $k_n = \dfrac{(-1)^n \Gamma(\alpha + \frac{1}{2}) \Gamma(2\alpha + n)}{2^n n! \Gamma(2\alpha) \Gamma(\alpha + n + \frac{1}{2})}$

9.14 Walsh functions

Throughout this section $0 \leqslant t \leqslant 1$.

9.14.1 Paley (or dyadic) ordering

$$\text{pal}(i, t) = \prod_{k=1}^{m} r(k, t)^{b_k}, \quad i = 0,1,2,\ldots, N-1 \quad (N = 2^n)$$

where the *Rademacher function* is

$$r(i, t) = \text{sign}[\sin(2^i \pi t)],$$

and where $b_k = 0$ or 1, given by the binary expression of i as

$$i = (b_m b_{m-1} \ldots b_1)_2$$
$$= b_m 2^{m-1} + b_{m-1} 2^{m-2} + \ldots + b_1 2^0$$

and $$m = 1 + (\text{greatest integer} \leqslant \log_2 i).$$

9.14.2 Sequency (or Walsh) ordering

$$\text{wal}(i, t) = \text{pal}[g(i), t]$$

where $g(i)$ is the *binary-to-Gray code* conversion of i, defined by $g(i) = (g_m g_{m-1} \dots g_2 g_1)_2$, where

$$g_j = b_j \oplus b_{j+1}, \quad 1 \leqslant j \leqslant m - 1; \quad g_m = b_m$$

and $\oplus$ denotes modulo 2 addition, i.e.

$$0 \oplus 0 = 0, \quad 0 \oplus 1 = 1, \quad 1 \oplus 0 = 1, \quad 1 \oplus 1 = 0.$$

For example, wal(17, t) = pal(25, t), since

$$17 = (1\ 0\ 0\ 0\ 1)_2 \text{ (binary)}; \quad g(17) = (1\ 1\ 0\ 0\ 1)_2 \text{ (Gray code)} = 25 \text{ (decimal)}$$

Even and odd functions

cal(k, t) = wal($2k$, t); sal(k, t) = wal($2k - 1$, t); $k = 1,2,\dots,\frac{1}{2}N$.

9.14.3 Hadamard (or Kronecker or lexicographic) ordering

$$\text{wal}_h(i, t) = \text{pal}[b(i), t]$$

where $b(i) = (b_1 b_2 \dots b_m)_2$ is the *bit-reversal* of i as an n-bit number. For example, when $n = 5$, $\text{wal}_h(6, t) = \text{pal}(12, t)$ since

$$6 = (0\ 0\ 1\ 1\ 0)_2, \quad b(6) = (0\ 1\ 1\ 0\ 0)_2 = 12 \text{ (decimal)}$$

9.14.4 Discrete form

Divide $0 \leqslant t \leqslant 1$ into N equal parts. The N values of $\text{wal}_h(k, t)$ on the intervals t_i : $i/N < t < (i + 1)/N$, $i = 0,1,2,\dots,N - 1$, are given by the $(k + 1)$th row of the $N \times N$ *Hadamard matrix* H_N, defined by

$$H_N = H_2 \otimes H_{N/2}, \quad H_2 = \begin{bmatrix} 1 & 1 \\ 1 & -1 \end{bmatrix}$$

where $\otimes$ denotes Kronecker product (Section 8.10).

The discrete Walsh functions are denoted by Wal, Pal, Sal, Cal.

9.14.5 Orthogonality relations

$$\int_0^1 \text{wal}(m, t)\text{wal}(n, t)dt = \delta_{nm}$$

$$\sum_{i=0}^{N-1} \text{Wal}(m, t_i)\text{Wal}(n, t_i) = N\delta_{nm}.$$

10. STATISTICS

10.1 Mean and variance

mean:	$\bar{x} = \frac{1}{N} \sum_{i=1}^{n} f_i x_i$

variance:	$v_x = \frac{1}{N} \sum_{i=1}^{n} f_i (x_i - \bar{x})^2 = \sum_{i=1}^{n} \frac{f_i x_i^2}{N} - \left(\sum_{i=1}^{n} \frac{f_i x_i}{N} \right)^2$
	$= \frac{1}{N} \sum_{i=1}^{n} f_i x_i^2 - \bar{x}^2$

where $N = \sum_{i=1}^{n} f_i$ = total number of values.

For *grouped data:*

n = number of classes

x_i = mid-point of i-th class

f_i = number of values in i-th class

For *ungrouped data:*

n = number of distinct values of x

f_i = number of times x_i occurs.

In particular, if each $f_i = 1$

mean:	$\bar{x} = \frac{1}{n} \sum_{i=1}^{n} x_i$

variance:	$v_x = \frac{1}{n} \sum_{i=1}^{n} (x_i - \bar{x})^2 = \sum_{i=1}^{n} \frac{x_i^2}{n} - \left(\sum_{i=1}^{n} \frac{x_i}{n} \right)^2$
	$= \frac{1}{n} \sum_{i=1}^{n} x_i^2 - \bar{x}^2$

for a set of values $x_1, x_2, \ldots, x_n$.

In all cases the *standard deviation* $\sigma = \sqrt{\text{variance}}$.

10.1.1 Change of origin and scale factor

Let $X_1 = k(x_1 - a)$, where the scale factor k and origin a are chosen for convenience.

$$\bar{x} = a + \bar{X}/k$$
$$v_x = V_x/k^2$$

where $\bar{X}$, V_x are the mean and variance of X_1.

10.2 Normal distribution

For x distributed normally with mean μ, variance σ^2

$$\text{probability density function} = \frac{1}{\sigma\sqrt{2\pi}}\, e^{-(x-\mu)^2/2\sigma^2}$$

The *standardised normal variate*

$$X = (x - \mu)/\sigma$$

has mean 0, variance 1 and density function:

$$\phi(X) = \frac{1}{\sqrt{2\pi}}\, e^{-X^2/2}$$

$$\Phi(u) = \int_{-\infty}^{u} \phi(X)\,dX$$
$$= \text{probability of } -\infty < X \leqslant u$$

$$\text{Error function} \quad \operatorname{erf} u = \frac{2}{\sqrt{\pi}} \int_0^u e^{-t^2}\, dt$$

In particular $\operatorname{erf}(\infty) = 1$.

10.3 Poisson distribution

For a discrete random variable x,

Probability that $(x = r)$ $P(x = r)$	=	$\frac{\mu^r}{r!} e^{-\mu}$
Mean value of x	=	μ
Variance of x	=	μ

10.4 Binomial distribution

If an experiment has only two possible outcomes, "success" probability p, and "failure", probability $q = 1-p$, then:

probability of exactly r successes in n independent trials	=	${}^nC_r\, p^r q^{n-r} = \frac{n!}{r!(n-r)!} p^r q^{n-r}$
mean number of successes	=	np
variance of number of successes	=	npq
variance of proportion of successes	=	pq/n

10.4.1 Approximations

If $np > 5$ and $nq > 5$, the binomial distribution is closely approximated by a normal distribution with mean np, variance npq.

If $n \geqslant 50$, $np < 5$, the binomial distribution is closely approximated by a Poisson distribution with $\mu = np$.

10.5 Correlation

10.5.1 Coefficient of correlation

For a bivariate distribution consisting of n different pairs (x_i, y_i), with corresponding frequency f_i, and $\sum_{i=1}^{n} f_i = N$, the *covariance* is

$$\text{cov}(x,y) = \frac{1}{N} \sum_{i=1}^{n} f_i(x_i - \bar{x})(y_i - \bar{y})$$
$$= \frac{1}{N} \sum_{i=1}^{n} f_i x_i y_i - \bar{x}\,\bar{y}$$

and *correlation coefficient* is

$$r = \frac{\text{cov}(x,y)}{\sigma_x \sigma_y}$$
$$= \frac{\Sigma f_i (x_i - \bar{x})(y_i - \bar{y})}{\sqrt{\left[\Sigma f_i (x_i - \bar{x})^2\right]\left[\Sigma f_i (y_i - \bar{y})^2\right]}}$$
$$= \frac{\Sigma f_i x_i y_i - (\Sigma f_i x_i)(\Sigma f_i y_i)/N}{\sqrt{\Sigma f_i x_i^2 - (\Sigma f_i x_i)^2/N}\ \sqrt{\Sigma f_i y_i^2 - (\Sigma f_i y_i)^2/N}}$$

all summations being from $i = 1$ to $i = n$.

10.5.2 Ranked data

If x_i, y_i are rankings (i.e. two permutations of $1,2,\ldots,n$) then the expression for r becomes:

$$\text{Rank correlation coefficient} = 1 - \frac{6 \sum_{i=1}^{n} (x_i - y_i)^2}{n(n^2 - 1)}$$

10.6 Linear regression

For n pairs (x_i, y_i), frequency f_i, the *line of regression* (or *estimation*) of y on x is

$$y - \bar{y} = \left[\text{cov}(x,y)/v_x\right](x - \bar{x})$$

Line of regression of x on y is

$$x - \bar{x} = \left[\text{cov}(x,y)/v_y\right](y - \bar{y})$$

11. LENGTHS, AREAS, VOLUMES, MOMENTS

11.1 General formulae

11.1.1 Length of plane curve

FORM

Explicit

$y = f(x)$ between $x = a$ and $x = b$ $\qquad \displaystyle\int_a^b \left[1 + \left(\frac{dy}{dx}\right)^2\right]^{1/2} dx$

$x = g(y)$ between $y = \alpha$ and $y = \beta$ $\qquad \displaystyle\int_\alpha^\beta \left[1 + \left(\frac{dx}{dy}\right)^2\right]^{1/2} dy$

Parametric $x = \phi(t)$, $y = \psi(t)$ between $t = t_1$ and $t = t_2$

$$\int_{t_1}^{t_2} \left[\left(\frac{d\phi}{dt}\right)^2 + \left(\frac{d\psi}{dt}\right)^2\right]^{1/2} dt \quad .$$

Polar $\qquad r = r(\theta)$ between $\theta = \theta_1$ and $\theta = \theta_2$ $\qquad \displaystyle\int_{\theta_1}^{\theta_2} \left[r^2 + \left(\frac{dr}{d\theta}\right)^2\right]^{1/2} d\theta$

11.1.2 Radius of curvature

cartesian form $\quad y = f(x)$, $\quad R = \left[1 + \left(\frac{dy}{dx}\right)^2\right]^{3/2} \Big/ (d^2y/dx^2)$

polar form $\quad r = r(\theta)$, $\quad R = \dfrac{\left[r^2 + \left(\frac{dr}{d\theta}\right)^2\right]^{3/2}}{r^2 + 2\left(\frac{dr}{d\theta}\right)^2 - r\left(\frac{d^2r}{d\theta^2}\right)}$

11.1.3 Plane area

under curve $y = f(x)$ between ordinates $x = a$, $x = b$

$$\int_a^b f(x)dx$$

of curvilinear sector between $\theta = \theta_1$, $\theta = \theta_2$ and $r = r(\theta)$

$$\tfrac{1}{2}\int_{\theta_1}^{\theta_2} r^2\, d\theta$$

11.1.4 Area of surface of revolution

generated by one complete revolution of the curve $y = f(x)$ about the x-axis between $x = a$ and $x = b$

$$2\pi \int_a^b y\left[1 + \left(\frac{dy}{dx}\right)^2\right]^{1/2} dx$$

11.1.5 Volume of solid of revolution in 11.1.4 is

$$\pi\int_a^b y^2\, dx$$

11.2 Particular cases

Rectangular cartesian coordinates are used throughout

11.2.1 Circle

Equation: $\qquad (x - a)^2 + (y - b)^2 = R^2$

or $\qquad x^2 + y^2 + 2gx + 2fy + c = 0$

centre $(a,b) \equiv (-g,-f)$ $\qquad$ radius $R = (g^2 + f^2 - c)^{1/2}$

Circumference $= 2\pi R$ $\qquad$ Area $= \pi R^2$

11.2.2 Sphere

Equation: $(x-a)^2 + (y-b)^2 + (z-c)^2 = R^2$

centre (a,b,c) radius R

Surface area $= 4\pi R^2$ Volume $= 4\pi R^3/3$

11.2.3 Ellipse

Equation: $x^2/a^2 + y^2/b^2 = 1$

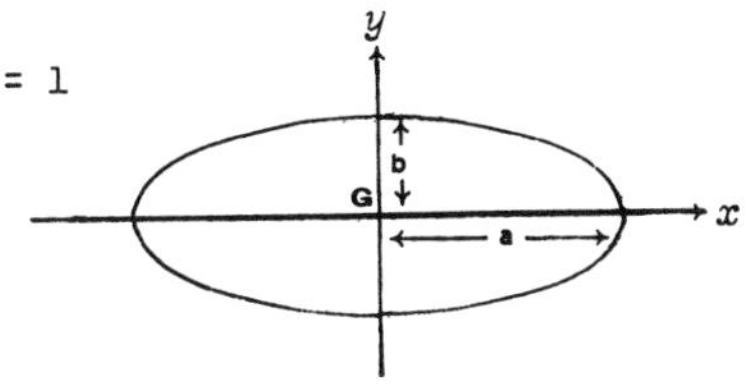

Eccentricity $e = (a^2 - b^2)^{1/2}/a$ Foci $(\pm ae, 0)$

Circumference $= 2\pi a\left[1 - \left(\frac{1}{2}\right)^2 e^2 - \left(\frac{1.3}{2.4}\right)^2 \frac{e^4}{3} - \left(\frac{1.3.5}{2.4.6}\right)^2 \frac{e^6}{5} - \ldots\right]$

Area $= \pi ab$

11.2.4 Ellipsoid

Equation: $\frac{x^2}{a^2} + \frac{y^2}{b^2} + \frac{z^2}{c^2} = 1$

Volume $= 4\pi abc/3$

11.2.5 Parabola

Equation: $y^2 = 4ax$

Focus $(a,0)$

Area $= 2bc/3$ $OG = 3b/5$

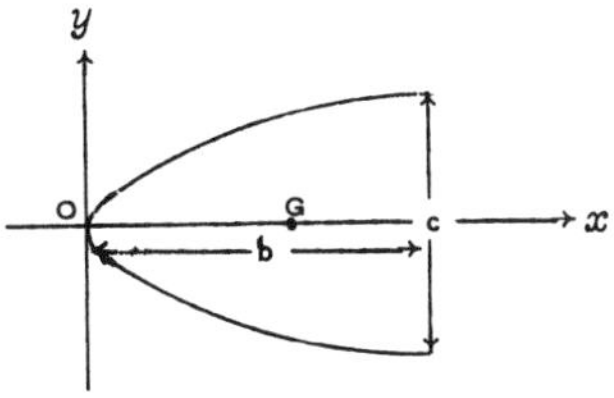

11.2.6 Right circular cone

Equation: $h^2(x^2 + y^2) = R^2 z^2$

Surface area $= \pi R\ell + \pi R^2$

Volume $= \pi R^2 h/3$ $OG = 3h/4$

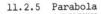

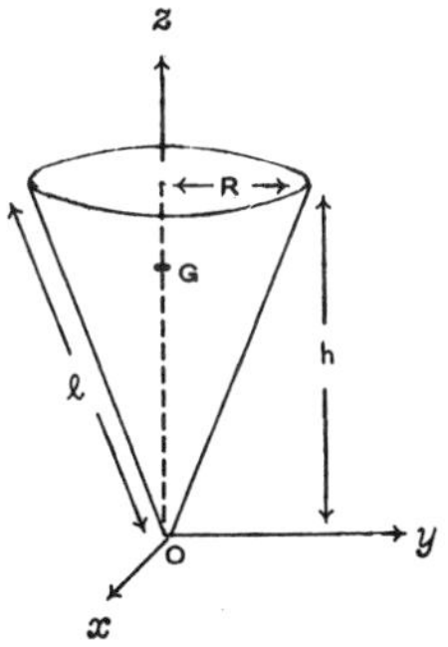

11.3 Theorems of Pappus

11.3.1 If a curve revolves about an axis which it does not intersect, the area of the surface swept out by the curve is equal to the product of the length of the curve and the length of the path traversed by the centre of gravity of the curve.

11.3.2 If an area revolves about an axis which it does not intersect, the volume generated is equal to the product of the area and the length of the path traversed by the centre of gravity of the area.

See 11.5 for some centres of gravity.

11.4 Moment of inertia: theorems

I_{OX} = moment of inertia of lamina or solid body about axis OX

$$= Mk_{OX}^2$$

where M = total mass, k_{OX} = *radius of gyration* about OX

11.4.1 Parallel axis theorem

If OX passes through the centre of gravity of the body, and $O'X'$ is parallel to OX and distant d from it, then

$$I_{O'X'} = I_{OX} + Md^2$$

11.4.2 Perpendicular axis theorem

If OX and OY are two mutually perpendicular axes in a lamina, passing through a point O, and OZ is perpendicular to the lamina, then

$$I_{OZ} = I_{OX} + I_{OY}$$

11.5 Radii of gyration

G denotes centre of gravity

11.5.1 Thin rod

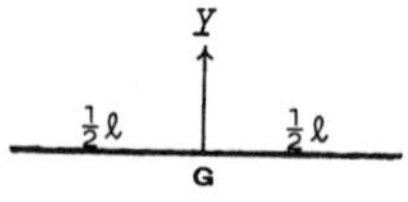

$$k_{GY}^2 = \frac{\ell^2}{12}$$

11.5.2 Thin rod in the shape of a circular arc

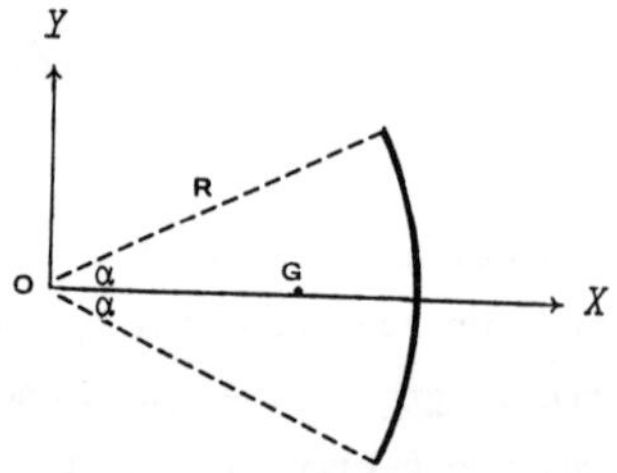

$$OG = \frac{R\sin\alpha}{\alpha}$$

$$k_{OX}^2 = \frac{R^2(\alpha - \sin\alpha\cos\alpha)}{2\alpha}$$

$$k_{OY}^2 = \frac{R^2(\alpha + \sin\alpha\cos\alpha)}{2\alpha}$$

11.5.3 Rectangular lamina

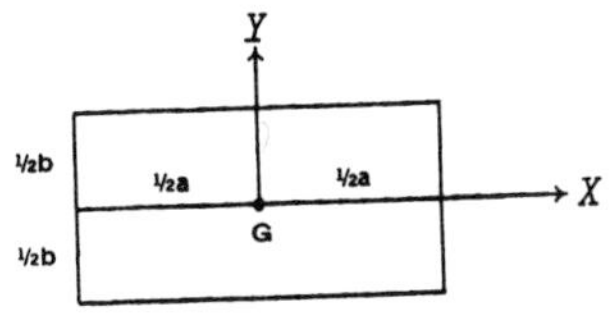

$$k_{OX}^2 = \frac{1}{12}b^2$$

11.5.4 Circular disk

Radius R, OX any diameter $k_{OX}^2 = \frac{1}{4}R^2$

11.5.5 Sector of circle

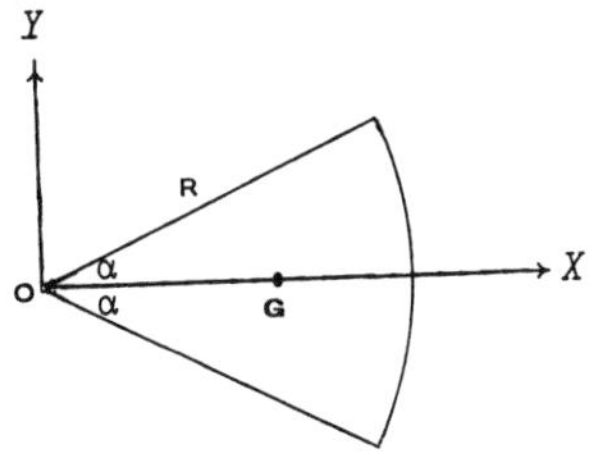

$$OG = \frac{2R\sin\alpha}{3\alpha}$$

$$k_{OX}^2 = \frac{R^2(\alpha - \sin\alpha\cos\alpha)}{4\alpha}$$

$$k_{OY}^2 = \frac{R^2(\alpha + \sin\alpha\cos\alpha)}{4\alpha}$$

11.5.6 Ellipse

See 11.2.3 $k_{GX}^2 = \frac{1}{4}b^2$

11.5.7 Rectangular prism

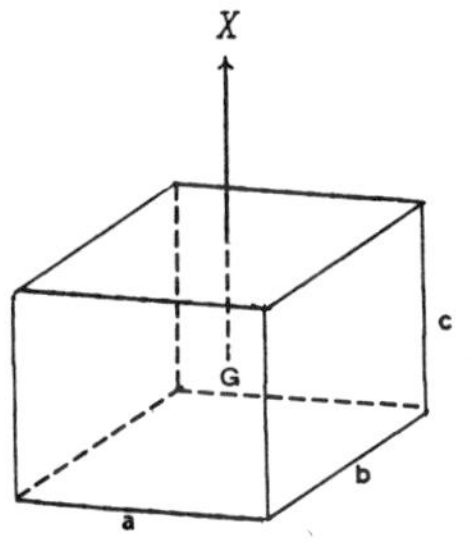

G is centre of prism

$$k_{GX}^2 = \frac{1}{12}(a^2 + b^2)$$

11.5.8 Sphere

Radius R, OX any diameter $k_{OX}^2 = \frac{2}{5}R^2$

11.5.9 Hemisphere

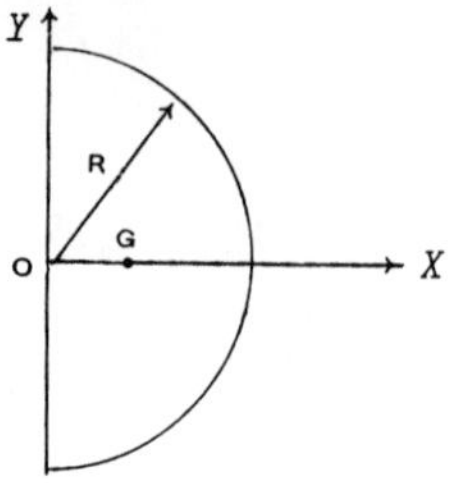

$OG = \frac{3}{8} R$

$k_{OX}^2 = k_{OY}^2 = \frac{2}{5} R^2$

11.5.10 Hemispherical shell

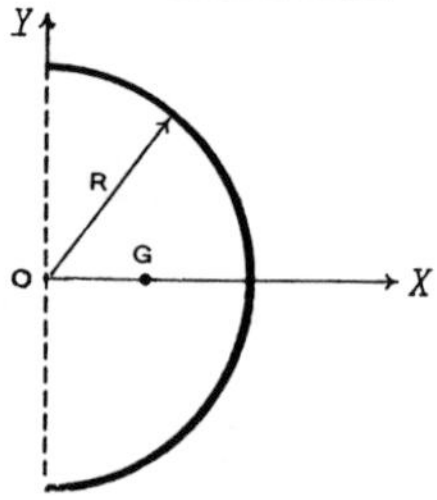

$OG = \frac{1}{2} R$

$k_{OX}^2 = k_{OY}^2 = \frac{2}{3} R^2$

11.5.11 Ellipsoid

See 11.2.3,4. $k_{Gx}^2 = (b^2 + c^2)/5$

11.5.12 Right circular cone

See 11.2.6 $OG = \frac{3}{4} h$ $k_{Oz}^2 = \frac{3R^2}{10}$

$k_{Ox}^2 = \frac{3(R^2 + 4h^2)}{20}$

11.5.13 Torus

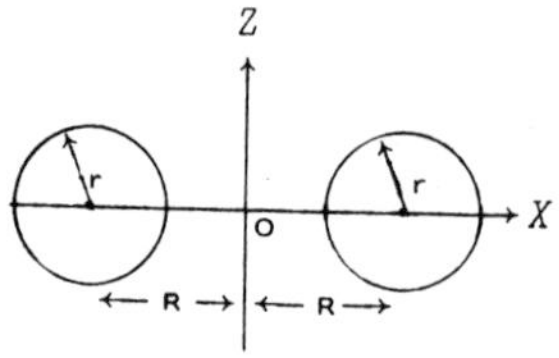

$k_{OZ}^2 = \frac{4R^2 + 3r^2}{4}$

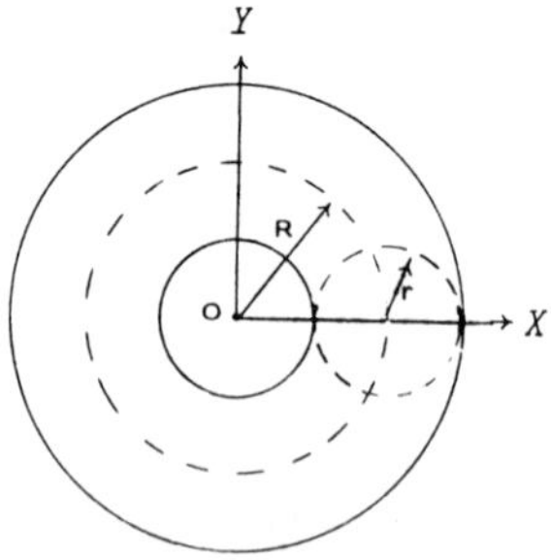

$k_{OX}^2 = \frac{4R^2 + 5r^2}{8}$

Area under the standard normal curve

$$\Phi(z_1) = \int_{-\infty}^{z_1} \frac{1}{\sqrt{(2\pi)}} \exp\left(-\frac{1}{2}z^2\right) dz$$

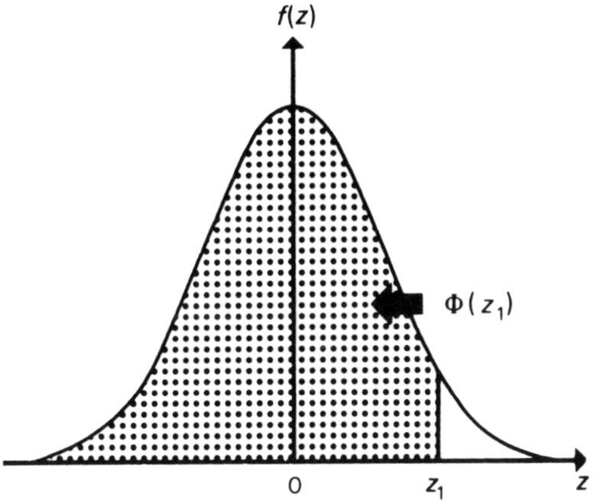

z	·00	·01	·02	·03	·04	·05	·06	·07	·08	·09
0·0	·5000	·5040	·5080	·5120	·5160	·5199	·5239	·5279	·5319	·5359
0·1	·5398	·5438	·5478	·5517	·5557	·5596	·5636	·5675	·5714	·5753
0·2	·5793	·5832	·5871	·5910	·5948	·5987	·6026	·6064	·6103	·6141
0·3	·6179	·6217	·6255	·6293	·6331	·6368	6406	·6443	·6480	·6517
0·4	·6554	·6591	·6628	·6664	·6700	·6736	·6772	·6808	·6844	·6879
0·5	·6915	·6950	·6985	·7019	·7054	·7088	·7123	·7157	·7190	·7224
0·6	·7257	·7291	·7324	·7357	·7389	·7422	·7454	·7486	·7517	·7549
0·7	·7580	·7611	·7642	·7673	·7704	·7734	·7764	·7794	·7823	·7852
0·8	·7881	·7910	·7939	·7967	·7995	·8023	·8051	·8078	·8106	·8133
0·9	·8159	·8186	·8212	·8238	·8264	·8289	·8315	·8340	·8365	·8389
1·0	·8413	·8438	·8461	·8485	·8508	·8531	·8554	·8577	·8599	·8621
1·1	·8643	·8665	·8686	·8708	·8729	·8749	·8770	·8790	·8810	·8830
1·2	·8849	·8869	·8888	·8907	·8925	·8944	·8962	·8980	·8997	·9015
1·3	·9032	·9049	·9066	·9082	·9099	·9115	·9131	·9147	·9162	·9177
1·4	·9192	·9207	·9222	·9236	·9251	·9265	·9279	·9292	·9306	·9319
1·5	·9332	·9345	·9357	·9370	·9382	·9394	·9406	·9418	·9429	·9441
1·6	·9452	·9463	·9474	·9484	·9495	·9505	·9515	·9525	·9535	·9545
1·7	·9554	·9564	·9573	·9582	·9591	·9599	·9608	·9616	·9625	·9633
1·8	·9641	·9649	·9656	·9664	·9671	·9678	·9686	·9693	·9699	·9706
1·9	·9713	·9719	·9726	·9732	·9738	·9744	·9750	·9756	·9761	·9767
2·0	·9772	·9778	·9783	·9788	·9793	·9798	·9803	·9808	·9812	·9817
2·1	·9821	·9826	·9830	·9834	·9838	·9842	·9846	·9850	·9854	·9857
2·2	·9861	·9864	·9868	·9871	·9875	·9878	·9881	·9884	·9887	·9890
2·3	·9893	·9896	·9898	·9901	·9904	·9906	·9909	·9911	·9913	·9916
2·4	·9918	·9920	·9922	·9925	·9927	·9929	·9931	·9932	·9934	·9936
2·5	·9938	·9940	·9941	·9943	·9945	·9946	·9948	·9949	·9951	·9952
2·6	·9953	·9955	·9956	·9957	·9959	·9960	·9961	·9962	·9963	·9964
2·7	·9965	·9966	·9967	·9968	·9969	·9970	·9971	·9972	·9973	·9974
2·8	·9974	·9975	·9976	·9977	·9977	·9978	·9979	·9979	·9980	·9981
2·9	·9981	·9982	·9982	·9983	·9984	·9984	·9985	·9985	·9986	·9986
3·0	·9987	·9987	·9987	·9988	·9988	·9989	·9989	·9989	·9990	·9990
3·1	·9990	·9991	·9991	·9991	·9992	·9992	·9992	·9992	·9993	·9993
3·2	·9993	·9993	·9994	·9994	·9994	·9994	·9994	·9995	·9995	·9995
3·3	·9995	·9995	·9995	·9996	·9996	·9996	·9996	·9996	·9996	·9997
3·4	·9997	·9997	·9997	·9997	·9997	·9997	·9997	·9997	·9997	·9998

z	3·5	3·6	3·7	3·8	3·9	4·0
Φ(z)	·99977	·99984	·99989	·99993	·99995	·99997

Percentage points of the t-distribution

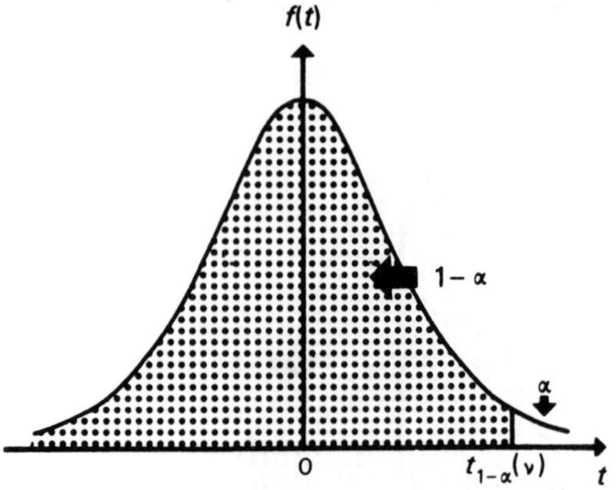

ν	$t_{0\cdot90}$	$t_{0\cdot95}$	$t_{0\cdot975}$	$t_{0\cdot99}$	$t_{0\cdot995}$	$t_{0\cdot9975}$	$t_{0\cdot999}$	$t_{0\cdot9995}$
1	3·078	6·314	12·706	31·821	63·657	127·32	318·31	636·62
2	1·886	2·920	4·303	6·965	9·925	14·089	22·327	31·598
3	1·638	2·353	3·182	4·541	5·841	7·453	10·214	12·924
4	1·533	2·132	2·776	3·747	4·604	5·598	7·173	8·610
5	1·476	2·015	2·571	3·365	4·032	4·773	5·893	6·869
6	1·440	1·943	2·447	3·143	3·707	4·317	5·208	5·959
7	1·415	1·895	2·365	2·998	3·499	4·029	4·785	5·408
8	1·397	1·860	2·306	2·896	3·355	3·833	4·501	5·041
9	1·383	1·833	2·262	2·821	3·250	3·690	4·297	4·781
10	1·372	1·812	2·228	2·764	3·169	3·581	4·144	4·587
11	1·363	1·796	2·201	2·718	3·106	3·497	4·025	4·437
12	1·356	1·782	2·179	2·681	3·055	3·428	3·930	4·318
13	1·350	1·771	2·160	2·650	3·012	3·372	3·852	4·221
14	1·345	1·761	2·145	2·624	2·977	3·326	3·787	4·140
15	1·341	1·753	2·131	2·602	2·947	3·286	3·733	4·073
16	1·337	1·746	2·120	2·583	2·921	3·252	3·686	4·015
17	1·333	1·740	2·110	2·567	2·898	3·222	3·646	3·965
18	1·330	1·734	2·101	2·552	2·878	3·197	3·610	3·922
19	1·328	1·729	2·093	2·539	2·861	3·174	3·579	3·883
20	1·325	1·725	2·086	2·528	2·845	3·153	3·552	3·850
21	1·323	1·721	2·080	2·518	2·831	3·135	3·527	3·819
22	1·321	1·717	2·074	2·508	2·819	3·119	3·505	3·792
23	1·319	1·714	2·069	2·500	2·807	3·104	3·485	3·767
24	1·318	1·711	2·064	2·492	2·797	3·091	3·467	3·745
25	1·316	1·708	2·060	2·485	2·787	3·078	3·450	3·725
26	1·315	1·706	2·056	2·479	2·779	3·067	3·435	3·707
27	1·314	1·703	2·052	2·473	2·771	3·057	3·421	3·690
28	1·313	1·701	2·048	2·467	2·763	3·047	3·408	3·674
29	1·311	1·699	2·045	2·462	2·756	3·038	3·396	3·659
30	1·310	1·697	2·042	2·457	2·750	3·030	3·385	3·646
40	1·303	1·684	2·021	2·423	2·704	2·971	3·307	3·551
60	1·296	1·671	2·000	2·390	2·660	2·915	3·232	3·460
120	1·289	1·658	1·980	2·358	2·617	2·860	3·160	3·373
∞	1·282	1·645	1·960	2·326	2·576	2·807	3·090	3·291

Percentage points of the χ^2 distribution

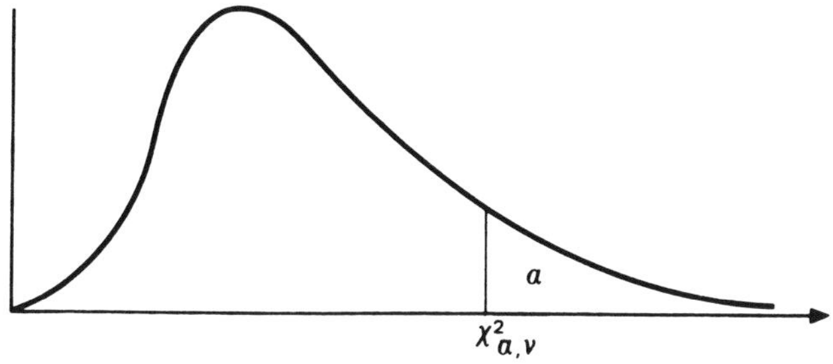

α	·995	·99	·975	·95	·50	·20	·10	·05	·025	·01	·005
ν											
1	0·000	0·0002	0·001	0·0039	0·45	1·64	2·71	3·84	5·02	6·63	7·88
2	0·010	0·020	0·051	0·103	1·39	3·22	4·61	5·99	7·38	9·21	10·60
3	0·072	0·115	0·216	0·352	2·37	4·64	6·25	7·81	9·35	11·34	12·84
4	0·207	0·30	0·484	0·71	3·36	5·99	7·78	9·49	11·14	13·28	14·86
5	0·412	0·55	0·831	1·15	4·35	7·29	9·24	11·07	12·83	15·09	16·75
6	0·676	0·87	1·24	1·64	5·35	8·56	10·64	12·59	14·45	16·81	18·55
7	0·989	1·24	1·69	2·17	6·35	9·80	12·02	14·07	16·01	18·48	20·28
8	1·34	1·65	2·18	2·73	7·34	11·03	13·36	15·51	17·53	20·09	21·95
9	1·73	2·09	2·70	3·33	8·34	12·24	14·68	16·92	19·02	21·67	23·59
10	2·16	2·56	3·25	3·94	9·34	13·44	15·99	18·31	20·48	23·21	25·19
11	2·60	3·05	3·82	4·57	10·34	14·63	17·28	19·68	21·92	24·72	26·76
12	3·07	3·57	4·40	5·23	11·34	15·81	18·55	21·03	23·34	26·22	28·30
13	3·57	4·11	5·01	5·89	12·34	16·98	19·81	22·36	24·74	27·69	29·82
14	4·07	4·66	5·63	6·57	13·34	18·15	21·06	23·68	26·12	29·14	31·32
15	4·60	5·23	6·26	7·26	14·34	19·31	22·31	25·00	27·49	30·58	32·80
16	5·14	5·81	6·91	7·96	15·34	20·47	23·54	26·30	28·85	32·00	34·27
17	5·70	6·41	7·56	8·67	16·34	21·61	24·77	27·59	30·19	33·41	35·72
18	6·26	7·02	8·23	9·39	17·34	22·76	25·99	28·87	31·53	34·81	37·16
19	6·84	7·63	8·91	10·12	18·34	23·90	27·20	30·14	32·85	36·19	38·58
20	7·43	8·26	9·59	10·85	19·34	25·04	28·41	31·41	34·17	37·57	40·00
21	8·03	8·90	10·28	11·59	20·34	26·17	29·62	32·67	35·48	38·93	41·40
22	8·64	9·54	10·98	12·34	21·34	27·30	30·81	33·92	36·78	40·29	42·80
23	9·26	10·20	11·69	13·09	23·34	28·43	32·01	35·17	38·08	41·64	44·18
24	9·89	10·86	12·40	13·85	23·34	29·55	33·20	36·42	39·36	42·98	45·56
25	10·52	11·52	13·12	14·61	24·34	30·68	34·38	37·65	40·65	44·31	46·93
26	11·16	12·20	13·84	15·38	25·34	31·79	35·56	38·89	41·92	45·64	48·29
27	11·81	12·88	14·57	16·15	26·34	32·91	36·74	40·11	43·19	46·96	49·64
28	12·46	13·57	15·31	16·93	27·34	34·03	37·92	41·34	44·46	48·28	50·99
29	13·12	14·26	16·05	17·71	28·34	35·14	39·09	42·56	45·72	49·59	52·34
30	13·79	14·95	16·79	18·49	29·34	36·25	40·26	43·77	46·98	50·89	53·67
40	20·71	22·16	24·43	26·51	39·34	47·27	51·81	55·76	59·34	63·69	66·77
50	27·99	29·71	32·36	34·76	49·33	58·16	63·17	67·50	71·41	76·15	79·49
60	35·53	37·48	40·48	43·19	59·33	68·97	74·40	79·08	83·30	88·38	91·95
70	43·28	45·44	48·76	51·74	69·33	79·71	85·53	90·53	95·02	100·43	104·2
80	51·17	53·54	57·15	60·39	79·33	90·41	96·58	101·88	106·63	112·33	116·3
90	59·20	61·75	65·65	69·13	89·33	101·05	107·57	113·15	118·14	124·12	128·3
100	67·33	70·06	74·22	77·93	99·33	111·67	118·50	124·34	129·56	135·81	140·2

Percentage points of the F-distribution, one tail

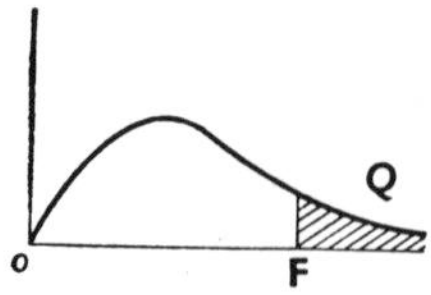

Q%	ν_2 \ ν_1	1	2	3	4	5	6	7	8	9	10	12	15	20	24	∞
5	1	161·4	199·5	215·7	224·6	230·2	234·0	236·8	238·9	240·5	241·9	243·9	246·0	248·0	249·1	254·3
1		4052	5000	5403	5625	5764	5859	5928	5982	6022	6056	6106	6157	6209	6235	6366
5	2	18·51	19·00	19·16	19·25	19·30	19·33	19·35	19·37	19·38	19·40	19·41	19·43	19·45	19·45	19·50
1		98·50	99·00	99·17	99·25	99·30	99·33	99·36	99·37	99·39	99·40	99·42	99·43	99·45	99·46	99·50
5	3	10·13	9·55	9·28	9·12	9·01	8·94	8·89	8·85	8·81	8·79	8·74	8·70	8·66	8·64	8·53
1		34·12	30·82	29·46	28·71	28·24	27·91	27·67	27·49	27·35	27·23	27·05	26·87	26·69	26·60	26·13
5	4	7·71	6·94	6·59	6·39	6·26	6·16	6·09	6·04	6·00	5·96	5·91	5·86	5·80	5·77	5·63
1		21·20	18·00	16·69	15·98	15·52	15·21	14·98	14·80	14·66	14·55	14·37	14·20	14·02	13·93	13·46
5	5	6·61	5·79	5·41	5·19	5·05	4·95	4·88	4·82	4·77	4·74	4·68	4·62	4·56	4·53	4·36
1		16·26	13·27	12·06	11·39	10·97	10·67	10·46	10·29	10·16	10·05	9·89	9·72	9·55	9·47	9·02
5	6	5·99	5·14	4·76	4·53	4·39	4·28	4·21	4·15	4·10	4·06	4·00	3·94	3·87	3·84	3·67
1		13·75	10·92	9·78	9·15	8·75	8·47	8·26	8·10	7·98	7·87	7·72	7·56	7·40	7·31	6·88
5	7	5·59	4·74	4·35	4·12	3·97	3·87	3·79	3·73	3·68	3·64	3·57	3·51	3·44	3·41	3·23
1		12·25	9·55	8·45	7·85	7·46	7·19	6·99	6·84	6·72	6·62	6·47	6·31	6·16	6·07	5·65
5	8	5·32	4·46	4·07	3·84	3·69	3·58	3·50	3·44	3·39	3·35	3·28	3·22	3·15	3·12	2·93
1		11·26	8·65	7·59	7·01	6·63	6·37	6·18	6·03	5·91	5·81	5·67	5·52	5·36	5·28	4·86
5	9	5·12	4·26	3·86	3·63	3·48	3·37	3·29	3·23	3·18	3·14	3·07	3·01	2·94	2·90	2·71
1		10·56	8·02	6·99	6·42	6·06	5·80	5·61	5·47	5·35	5·26	5·11	4·96	4·81	4·73	4·31
5	10	4·96	4·10	3·71	3·48	3·33	3·22	3·14	3·07	3·02	2·98	2·91	2·85	2·77	2·74	2·54
1		10·04	7·56	6·55	5·99	5·64	5·39	5·20	5·06	4·94	4·85	4·71	4·56	4·41	4·33	3·91
5	11	4·84	3·98	3·59	3·36	3·20	3·09	3·01	2·95	2·90	2·85	2·79	2·72	2·65	2·61	2·40
1		9·65	7·21	6·22	5·67	5·32	5·07	4·89	4·74	4·63	4·54	4·40	4·25	4·10	4·02	3·60
5	12	4·75	3·89	3·49	3·26	3·11	3·00	2·91	2·85	2·80	2·75	2·69	2·62	2·54	2·51	2·30
1		9·33	6·93	5·95	5·41	5·06	4·82	4·64	4·50	4·39	4·30	4·16	4·01	3·86	3·78	3·36
5	13	4·67	3·81	3·41	3·18	3·03	2·92	2·83	2·77	2·71	2·67	2·60	2·53	2·46	2·42	2·21
1		9·07	6·70	5·74	5·21	4·86	4·62	4·44	4·30	4·19	4·10	3·96	3·82	3·66	3·59	3·17
5	14	4·60	3·74	3·34	3·11	2·96	2·85	2·76	2·70	2·65	2·60	2·53	2·46	2·39	2·35	2·13
1		8·86	6·51	5·56	5·04	4·69	4·46	4·28	4·14	4·03	3·94	3·80	3·66	3·51	3·43	3·00
5	15	4·54	3·68	3·29	3·06	2·90	2·79	2·71	2·64	2·59	2·54	2·48	2·40	2·33	2·29	2·07
1		8·68	6·36	5·42	4·89	4·56	4·32	4·14	4·00	3·89	3·80	3·67	3·52	3·37	3·29	2·87
5	16	4·49	3·63	3·24	3·01	2·85	2·74	2·66	2·59	2·54	2·49	2·42	2·35	2·28	2·24	2·01
1		8·53	6·23	5·29	4·77	4·44	4·20	4·03	3·89	3·78	3·69	3·55	3·41	3·26	3·18	2·75
5	17	4·45	3·59	3·20	2·96	2·81	2·70	2·61	2·55	2·49	2·45	2·38	2·31	2·23	2·19	1·96
1		8·40	6·11	5·18	4·67	4·34	4·10	3·93	3·79	3·68	3·59	3·46	3·31	3·16	3·08	2·65
5	18	4·41	3·55	3·16	2·93	2·77	2·66	2·58	2·51	2·46	2·41	2·34	2·27	2·19	2·15	1·92
1		8·29	6·01	5·09	4·58	4·25	4·01	3·84	3·71	3·60	3·51	3·37	3·23	3·08	3·00	2·57
5	19	4·38	3·52	3·13	2·90	2·74	2·63	2·54	2·48	2·42	2·38	2·31	2·23	2·16	2·11	1·88
1		8·18	5·93	5·01	4·50	4·17	3·94	3·77	3·63	3·52	3·43	3·30	3·15	3·00	2·92	2·49
5	20	4·35	3·49	3·10	2·87	2·71	2·60	2·51	2·45	2·39	2·35	2·28	2·20	2·12	2·08	1·84
1		8·10	5·85	4·94	4·43	4·10	3·87	3·70	3·56	3·46	3·37	3·23	3·09	2·94	2·86	2·42
5	21	4·32	3·47	3·07	2·84	2·68	2·57	2·49	2·42	2·37	2·32	2·25	2·18	2·10	2·05	1·81
1		8·02	5·78	4·87	4·37	4·04	3·81	3·64	3·51	3·40	3·31	3·17	3·03	2·88	2·80	2·36
5	22	4·30	3·44	3·05	2·82	2·66	2·55	2·46	2·40	2·34	2·30	2·23	2·15	2·07	2·03	1·78
1		7·95	5·72	4·82	4·31	3·99	3·76	3·59	3·45	3·35	3·26	3·12	2·98	2·83	2·75	2·31
5	23	4·28	3·42	3·03	2·80	2·64	2·53	2·44	2·37	2·32	2·27	2·20	2·13	2·05	2·01	1·76
1		7·88	5·66	4·76	4·26	3·94	3·71	3·54	3·41	3·30	3·21	3·07	2·93	2·78	2·70	2·26
5	24	4·26	3·40	3·01	2·78	2·62	2·51	2·42	2·36	2·30	2·25	2·18	2·11	2·03	1·98	1·73
1		7·82	5·61	4·72	4·22	3·90	3·67	3·50	3·36	3·26	3·17	3·03	2·89	2·74	2·66	2·21
5	∞	3·84	3·00	2·60	2·37	2·21	2·10	2·01	1·94	1·88	1·83	1·75	1·67	1·57	1·52	1·00
1		6·63	4·61	3·78	3·32	3·02	2·80	2·64	2·51	2·41	2·32	2·18	2·04	1·88	1·79	1·00

Percentage points of the F-distribution, two tails

$Q = Q_1 + Q_2$

$Q_1 = Q_2$

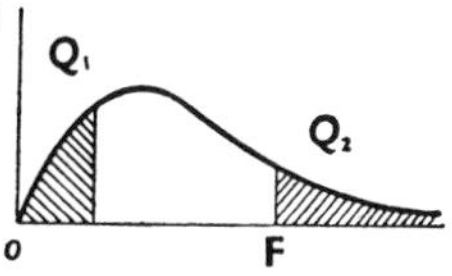

Q%	ν_2 \ ν_1	1	2	3	4	5	6	7	8	9	10	12	15	20	24	∞
5	1	647·8	799·5	864·2	899·6	921·8	937·1	948·2	956·7	963·3	968·6	976·7	984·9	993·1	997·2	1018
1	1	16211	20000	21615	22500	23056	23437	23715	23925	24091	24224	24426	24630	24836	24940	25465
5	2	38·51	39·00	39·17	39·25	39·30	39·33	39·36	39·37	39·39	39·40	39·41	39·43	39·45	39·46	39.50
1	2	198·5	199·0	199·2	199·2	199·3	199·3	199·4	199·4	199·4	199·4	199·4	199·4	199·4	199·5	199·5
5	3	17·44	16·04	15·44	15·10	14·88	14·73	14·62	14·54	14·47	14·42	14·34	14·25	14·17	14·12	13·90
1	3	55·55	49·80	47·47	46·20	45·39	44·84	44·43	44·13	43·88	43·69	43·39	43·08	42·78	42·62	41·83
5	4	12·22	10·65	9·98	9·60	9·36	9·20	9·07	8·98	8·90	8·84	8·75	8·66	8·56	8·51	8·26
1	4	31·33	26·28	24·26	23·15	22·46	21·97	21·62	21·35	21·14	20·97	20·70	20·44	20·17	20·03	19·32
5	5	10·01	8·43	7·76	7·39	7·15	6·98	6·85	6·76	6·68	6·62	6·52	6·43	6·33	6·28	6·02
1	5	22·78	18·31	16·53	15·56	14·94	14·51	14·20	13·96	13·77	13·62	13·38	13·15	12·90	12·78	12·14
5	6	8·81	7·26	6·60	6·23	5·99	5·82	5·70	5·60	5·52	5·46	5·37	5·27	5·17	5·12	4·85
1	6	18·63	14·54	12·92	12·03	11·46	11·07	10·79	10·57	10·39	10·25	10·03	9·81	9·59	9·47	8·88
5	7	8·07	6·54	5·89	5·52	5·29	5·12	4·99	4·90	4·82	4·76	4·67	4·57	4·47	4·42	4·14
1	7	16·24	12·40	10·88	10·05	9·52	9·16	8·89	8·68	8·51	8·38	8·18	7·97	7·75	7·64	7·08
5	8	7·57	6·06	5·42	5·05	4·82	4·65	4·53	4·43	4·36	4·30	4·20	4·10	4·00	3·95	3·67
1	8	14·69	11·04	9·60	8·81	8·30	7·95	7·69	7·50	7·34	7·21	7·01	6·81	6·61	6·50	5·95
5	9	7·21	5·71	5·08	4·72	4·48	4·32	4·20	4·10	4·03	3·96	3·87	3·77	3·67	3·61	3·33
1	9	13·61	10·11	8·72	7·96	7·47	7·13	6·88	6·69	6·54	6·42	6·23	6·03	5·83	5·73	5·19
5	10	6·94	5·46	4·83	4·47	4·26	4·07	3·95	3·85	3·78	3·72	3·62	3·52	3·42	3·37	3·08
1	10	12·83	9·43	8·08	7·34	6·87	6·54	6·30	6·12	5·97	5·85	5·66	5·47	5·27	5·17	4·64
5	11	6·72	5·26	4·63	4·28	4·04	3·88	3·76	3·66	3·59	3·53	3·43	3·33	3·23	3·17	2·88
1	11	12·23	8·91	7·60	6·88	6·42	6·10	5·86	5·68	5·54	5·42	5·24	5·05	4·86	4·76	4·23
5	12	6·55	5·10	4·47	4·12	3·89	3·73	3·61	3·51	3·44	3·37	3·28	3·18	3·07	3·02	2·72
1	12	11·75	8·51	7·23	6·52	6·07	5·76	5·52	5·35	5·20	5·09	4·91	4·72	4·53	4·43	3·90
5	13	6·41	4·97	4·35	4·00	3·77	3·60	3·48	3·39	3·31	3·25	3·15	3·05	2·95	2·89	2·60
1	13	11·37	8·19	6·93	6·23	5·79	5·48	5·25	5·08	4·94	4·82	4·64	4·46	4·27	4·17	3·65
5	14	6·30	4·86	4·24	3·89	3·66	3·50	3·38	3·29	3·21	3·15	3·05	2·95	2·84	2·79	2·49
1	14	11·06	7·92	6·68	6·00	5·56	5·26	5·03	4·86	4·72	4·60	4·43	4·25	4·06	3·96	3·44
5	15	6·20	4·77	4·15	3·80	3·58	3·41	3·29	3·20	3·12	3·06	2·96	2·86	2·76	2·70	2·40
1	15	10·80	7·70	6·48	5·80	5·37	5·07	4·85	4·67	4·54	4·42	4·25	4·07	3·88	3·79	3·26
5	16	6·12	4·69	4·08	3·73	3·50	3·34	3·22	3·12	3·05	2·99	2·89	2·79	2·68	2·63	2·32
1	16	10·58	7·51	6·30	5·64	5·21	4·91	4·69	4·52	4·38	4·27	4·10	3·92	3·73	3·64	3·11
5	17	6·04	4·62	4·01	3·66	3·44	3·28	3·16	3·06	2·98	2·92	2·82	2·72	2·62	2·56	2·25
1	17	10·38	7·35	6·16	5·50	5·07	4·78	4·56	4·39	4·25	4·14	3·97	3·79	3·61	3·51	2·98
5	18	5·98	4·56	3·95	3·61	3·38	3·22	3·10	3·01	2·93	2·87	2·77	2·67	2·56	2·50	2·19
1	18	10·22	7·21	6·03	5·37	4·96	4·66	4·44	4·28	4·14	4·03	3·86	3·68	3·50	3·40	2·87
5	19	5·92	4·51	3·90	3·56	3·33	3·17	3·05	2·96	2·88	2·82	2·72	2·62	2·51	2·45	2·13
1	19	10·07	7·09	5·92	5·27	4·85	4·56	4·34	4·18	4·04	3·93	3·76	3·59	3·40	3·31	2·78
5	20	5·87	4·46	3·86	3·51	3·29	3·13	3·01	2·91	2·84	2·77	2·68	2·57	2·46	2·41	2·09
1	20	9·94	6·99	5·82	5·17	4·76	4·47	4·26	4·09	3·96	3·85	3·68	3·50	3·32	3·22	2·69
5	21	5·83	4·42	3·82	3·48	3·25	3·09	2·97	2·87	2·80	2·73	2·64	2·53	2·42	2·37	2·04
1	21	9·83	6·89	5·73	5·09	4·68	4·39	4·18	4·01	3·88	3·77	3·60	3·43	3·24	3·15	2·61
5	22	5·79	4·38	3·78	3·44	3·22	3·05	2·93	2·84	2·76	2·70	2·60	2·50	2·39	2·33	2·00
1	22	9·73	6·81	5·65	5·02	4·61	4·32	4·11	3·94	3·81	3·70	3·54	3·36	3·18	3·08	2·55
5	23	5·75	4·35	3·75	3·41	3·18	3·02	2·90	2·81	2·73	2·67	2·57	2·47	2·36	2·30	1·97
1	23	9·63	6·73	5·58	4·95	4·54	4·26	4·05	3·88	3·75	3·64	3·47	3·30	3·12	3·02	2·48
5	24	5·72	4·32	3·72	3·38	3·15	2·99	2·87	2·78	2·70	2·64	2·54	2·44	2·33	2·27	1·94
1	24	9·55	6·66	5·52	4·89	4·49	4·20	3·99	3·83	3·69	3·59	3·42	3·25	3·06	2·97	2·43
5	∞	5·02	3·69	3·12	2·79	2·57	2·41	2·29	2·19	2·11	2·05	1·94	1·83	1·71	1·64	1·00
1	∞	7·88	5·30	4·28	3·72	3·35	3·09	2·90	2·74	2·62	2·52	2·36	2·19	2·00	1·90	1·00

INDEX

Section numbers are given in parentheses